THE WINES
Bergerac

Phil Hargreaves

Highgate
Publications

The Wines of
Bergerac

By Phil Hargreaves

First published in the United Kingdom in 2008 by Highgate Publications Ltd.

ISBN 978-1-902645-51-3

A CIP catalogue record for this book is available from the British Library.

Although all reasonable care has been taken in the preparation of this book, neither the publisher nor the author can accept any liability for any consequences arising from its use or from the information it contains. As far as could be ascertained, all details were correct at the time of going to press.

Artwork by Core Print & Design Services Ltd
Printed by Core Print & Design Services Ltd
Published by Highgate Publications Ltd.
24, Wylies Road, Beverley, HU17 7AP. Tel: 01482-866826

Contents

Acknowledgements/Photographs - 4
Foreword - 5
Introduction - 7
A Slice of History - 9

The Appellations - 12
Bergerac - 12
Monbazillac - 14
Montravel - 15
Pécharmant - 16
Rosette - 17
Saussignac - 18
Grape Varieties - 19
From Vine to Wine - 21
Recent Vintages - 24
How to use this guide - 27

The Producers - 29
Pécharmant/Rosette - 31
Monbazillac (East) - 45
Monbazillac (West) - 63
Saussignac - 83
Montravel - 107
Eymet-Issigeac-Lalinde - 127

Glossary - 137
Bibliography - 141
Index of Owners/Winemakers - 143
Index of Properties - 147
About the Author - 151

Acknowledgements

First and foremost, I must thank all the winemakers who have co-operated over the production of this guide. I know just how busy they are and appreciate the time they have afforded me and the wines they have provided. One of my starting points was to contact the British winemakers who are established out there in the Dordogne and I am grateful to Hugh Ryman, Charles Martin, Olivia Donnan and especially Patricia Atkinson for all the encouragement they gave me in the early stages.

I have received invaluable information from the I.N.A.O. and the C.I.V.R.B. and would especially thank Xavier de la Verrie at the latter for his help and his patience.

It was a mammoth task tasting our way through about 400 wines for this guide and I owe a big debt of gratitude to my tasting team which was drawn from experienced tasters at the Premier Cru Wine Club and especially the Hengate Wine School. Funnily enough, we did not disagree violently about too many of the wines and I know they were impressed by the overall high standard and value for money of the wines we tasted.

Finally, I would like to thank my wife Claude for her constant support, her IT wizardry, the proof reading, the photos and her tolerance of the hours I spent at the computer.

Photographs

Photograph of "Foncaussade" which appears on the front cover is used by kind permission of the Cave de Sigoulès, photographer Garry Timms.

Photographs of grapes courtesy of Château Kalian.

I am grateful to the following properties for supplying their own illustrations: Champarel, Chemins d'Orient, Grand Jaure, Haut-Pécharmant, Terre Vieille, Les Merles, Briand, Clos l'Envège, Kalian, Petit Paris, Poulvère, Belingard, Borie Blanche, Boyer, Grange Neuve, Haut Lamouthe, Haut Montlong, Le Mayne, Moulin Pouzy, Cave de Sigoulès, Brandeaux, Cantonnet, La Colline, Les Eyssards, Haut Garrigue, Clos du Mège, Monestier La Tour, Grimardy, Julien, Mallevieille, Moulin Garreau, Pique-Sègue, Union Vinicole Bergerac-Le Fleix, Breil, Saintongers d'Hautefeuille, Siorac.

All other photographs by Phil and Claude Hargreaves.

Foreword

With its vineyards adjoining those of Bordeaux, Bergerac has always struggled to emerge from the shadows of its more illustrious neighbour. For generations the wines of Bergerac have been seen as the poor relation in this part of South West France - growing the same grape varieties as Bordeaux on similar soil, but without the illustrious top names that lend the region a sheen of elegance.

But Bergerac has its own charms and is now seeing a resurgence in the quality of its wines. Neglected properties are being revived, old untidy vineyards are being replanted and wines that were good only for drinking locally are now finding markets overseas.

All this, in part, is because of a new generation of growers who now occupy the historic properties of this region. Many have come from outside the area, some from overseas, bringing investment, new enthusiasm and a wider perspective than was possible just a generation ago. In cases where family-owned properties have been handed down to the younger generation, they have prepared in a way their fathers could not have done, by working overseas and gaining experience in producing quality wine.

The result is that Bergerac is on the brink of a new wave, still with its history and traditions intact, but now once again prepared to take advantage of its unique landscape, climate, grapes and soil to make quality wines that run the whole range from dry whites, through rosés, reds and glorious mouth-filling sweet whites.

Phil Hargreaves has journeyed around Bergerac and its smaller districts of Monbazillac, Montravel, Pécharmant, Rosette and Saussignac, talking to growers, tasting the wines and examining how this new wave of dynamism is changing the face of this small corner of France. Now ready to emerge from the shadows, Bergerac is once again a region that is worth exploring for its quality wines, its glorious food and its inimitable style.

Christine Austin

Wine Writer for The Yorkshire Post
Louis Roederer Regional Wine Writer of the Year 2006

Introduction

If you asked the English what they thought of Bergerac, most over-fifties would probably make some reference to actor John Nettles, 40,000 plus would talk of their home or at least a holiday in the Dordogne and vying for third place would be the literati who have read "Cyrano" and the enlightened few who have already awoken to the quality of Bergerac wines. However, things are set to change. For too long Bergerac has bumped along in the wake of its more famous neighbour Bordeaux. Now top producers are leading the way in putting Bergerac back on the map. The hope is that top estate names will create an identity and a reputation for Bergerac as a whole. There are many good producers in the Dordogne, some exporting throughout the world, others, for whatever reasons, producing equally good wines but which are only available locally and have not yet crossed the Channel. What is certain is that there are some exciting wines out there in the depths of the Périgord, but you might have to go and find them yourself. Of the 92 producers listed, over half do not yet export to the U.K.

I have compiled this guide over the past year but my love affair with the Dordogne started some forty years ago when I was a student in Périgueux in 1968. A few years later, my late father-in-law introduced me to the wines of Cahors and Bergerac and the seed was sown for an interest in wines that would lead to twenty years in the wine trade and ultimately, this little book.

I have personally visited the vast majority of the producers in this guide and wines from every winemaker included have been tasted by myself and my tasting team, drawn from friends and colleagues at the Hengate Wine School and the Premier Cru Wine Club, based in Beverley, East Yorkshire. I have resisted the temptation to give wines a star rating as I recognise that taste in wine is a very personal thing and it does not pay to be too dogmatic. However, I hope the tasting comments will help you establish which wines will most appeal to you.

In any case, part of the fun of wine tourism is trying different styles and the relatively small area of the Bergerac vineyard offers a huge range of different types of wine. Whether you are interested in the sweet wines of Monbazillac and Saussignac or the reds of Pécharmant and Montravel, what unites all winemakers is their passion for making the best wine possible from their own particular terroir. Pascal Cuisset, for example, of Château des Eyssards, has no time for "Grandes Cuvées" and prefers to make wines that will give pleasure to as many people as possible, wines for the people. Luc de Conti, who currently exports to 90 countries worldwide, aims to make "des vins qui me touchent, qui me font des émotions." He remains upbeat about the future of Bergerac wines, an optimism that it is easy to share in spite of the difficult situation facing French wines at the moment. Perhaps it is appropriate to end with a few lines from Patricia Atkinson's best-selling "The Ripening Sun" about her adventure at Clos d'Yvigne and her beginnings in the Dordogne where she is now a popular and respected winemaker, a few lines which suggest all the magic associated with growing vines in this lovely part of France.

"In front of me are rows and rows of vines. Graceful, sinuous curves, architectural in form, their large leaves lush and green, protecting and nourishing, soaking up the sun and sweetening the harvest. The sun shines, hot and relentless, onto the grapes. They hang like jewels, perfectly crafted. Each vine represents the march of time, the past, the present and the future."

A Slice of History

Maybe, just for a change, we should talk about Britain's special relationship with the Dordogne. Some 40,000 ex-pats have made their home there in the last few years as they have discovered the charms of the Périgord's rolling hills, its equitable climate, prehistoric gems and gastronomic delights. But our links with this corner of rural France go back a long way, to Eleanor of Aquitaine in fact who married the French king, Louis VII, in 1137 only to be given the royal boot in 1152 when she promptly remarried Henry II Plantagenet, future king of England and took her lands in Aquitaine with her. The Bergerac wine trade with England prospered during this time and in 1254, Henry III of England and Duke of Aquitaine allowed the people of Bergerac to export their wines direct from Libourne without interference from the Bordelais and also exempted Bergerac wines from import taxes levied in England.

However, wine had been made in the region since Roman times, wine amphoras having been found at a Petrocorii settlement at what is now Coulounieix-Chamiers and elsewhere along the valley of the Dordogne. There is evidence too at the Roman villa at Montcaret that wine was being made in the first century but it is about a thousand years later that the industry really flourished under the monks of the Priory of Saint Martin near Bergerac who cultivated vines on the hill of Mont-Bazailhac. Indeed, legend has it that it was these Benedictine monks who first discovered noble rot, quite by accident of course, having rather neglected their vines.

In 1322, the "Vinée" of Bergerac was recognised, the officially delimited area of the vineyard, initially to the north of Bergerac, covering some 10 to 15 kilometres to include Ginestet, Maurens, Campsegret, Lembras, Creysse and Mouleydier. This privileged area was extended in 1495 to include villages on the left bank, namely Montcuq, Saint Mayme, Pomport, St Laurent des Vignes, Monbazillac, Colombier and St Christophe. Wines from this area were called "Entrée" wines and took priority over wines produced outside which were not allowed into the town or port of Bergerac until after Christmas. In times of conflict, security was assured in the vineyards of the "Vinée" with soldiers being placed on guard. And conflict there was. If you visit the Château de Sanxet, a pile of cannonballs is a stark reminder that the Hundred Years War started not far away at Montcuq near Monbazillac in 1345 with the arrival of an English army under the Earl of Derby, the future Duke of Lancaster and cousin of King Edward III. He caught the French off guard, capturing Bergerac and many towns and castles including La Réole. There was sporadic fighting in the Périgord but a truce was agreed at Périgueux in 1374 between John of Gaunt and du Guesclin only for the latter to invade Guyenne three years later. Seneschal Sir Thomas Felton was defeated and taken prisoner at Eymet and Bergerac fell but the Guyennois remained loyal to the Plantagenets. Thirty years later, at the turn of the century, the cities of Guyenne were still loyal to the Lancastrians and even when occupied by the French, Bergerac appealed to the English for protection. It is difficult to imagine what life must have been like for those working in the vineyards in those difficult times. We do know that many vineyards in the south-west were abandoned because of devastation by the French and that wine in England was now costing twice as much, partly because shipments from Bordeaux needed armed escorts. On July 17th 1453, some thirty miles down the road from where the conflict started, the ageing Talbot was defeated by the French at Castillon and the Hundred Years War was over. Aquitaine returned to the French after over 300 years in English hands.

By the middle of the sixteenth century, Bergerac had become a prosperous town, possessing as it did the only bridge over the Dordogne with a regular traffic of "gabares"[1] passing down the river from the Massif Central to Bordeaux. It became an important cultural centre and attracted many Huguenots to the town, becoming a protestant stronghold. In 1565 Bergerac received the young King Charles IX and his mother Catherine de Medicis and they were served "maintes pipes de vin blanc de Bergerac"[2]. This was the same king who seven years later, on August 24th 1572, ordered the St. Bartholomew's Day massacre when many protestant leaders were assassinated. France was being torn apart by the Wars of Religion and nowhere was the bitterness between Catholic and Protestant more evident than in the Dordogne where protestant Bergerac was opposed by the Catholics of Périgueux. In 1577 a ceasefire was agreed at Bergerac and Monbazillac was served as a "vin de paix." In 1580, agreement was reached at Le Fleix between Henri de Navarre and Henri III which served as a basis for the Edict of Nantes in 1598. When Henri de Navarre was crowned King of France in 1594, he said of Bergerac:" Bonne cuisine et grands vins, voilà le paradis sur terre"[3].

Bergerac remained fiercely protestant and with the revocation of the Edict of Nantes in 1685, some 300,000 inhabitants fled in exile to Germany, Switzerland and particularly Holland.

Not surprisingly therefore, in subsequent years, the wine trade with these countries of Northern Europe flourished to such an extent that the notion of "grands crus" first came into being in the form of "Marques Hollandaises", some of the best wines that were exported to the Dutch market. Many of these properties still exist today. To give some idea of the extent of trade at this time, there were in 1724 a total of 74 coopers in Bergerac, 14 in Saint Martin and another 11 in Montcuq and Monbazillac. Later in the century, the export of red wines developed too as there was a taste for "clairet" style wines but also heavier "black wines" so wines were produced to suit the market. The areas of Pécharmant and Boisse were important in this respect, with elderberries sometimes being added for extra colour at the request of the Nordic countries.

In 1816, topographist A. Julien produced the first classification of wines to include Bergerac, which has become known as "Le Julien". In it, wines from Monbazillac, St. Nessans and Sancé were in the second class along with Langon and Cérons, and just behind Sauternes and Barsac. Reds such as Pécharmant were in the third class alongside the likes of Pauillac, Margaux and the rest of the Médoc.

However, towards the end of the century, in common with the rest of Europe, the vineyards of Bergerac were devastated by the phylloxera louse. The only solution was to replant with resistant American rootstock but a measure of the damage caused can be seen in the figures. There were 107,000 hectares of vines in the region in 1865 but by the end of the century this had fallen to just 2,180 and many had turned instead to tobacco, walnuts and truffles. The first years of the 20th century were full of uncertainty. There was endless wrangling about the position of Bergerac and its wines vis-à-vis the Bordeaux vineyard until it was decided that the Bordeaux limits should coincide with the departmental boundaries of the Gironde. Bergerac and Marmande were left out on a limb but these were the first moves towards an "appellation contrôlée" system which would finally come with the setting up of the INAO (Institut National des Appellations d'Origine) in 1935.

[1] *large flat-bottomed boats used for transporting goods*

[2] *many pipes of Bergerac white wine*

[3] *good food and fine wine, it is paradise on earth*

The Appellations

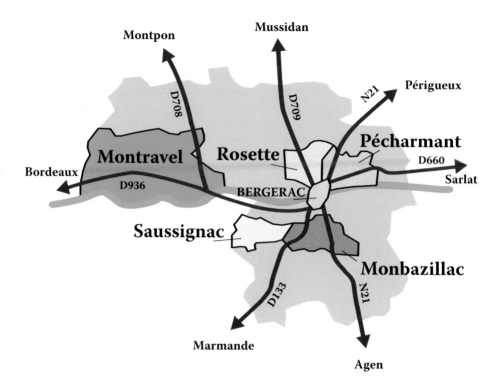

BERGERAC

Bergerac is situated in the south-west of France in the Dordogne department and its vineyards are a continuation of Bordeaux's Côtes de Castillon and St. Emilion on the right bank of the Dordogne, and the Entre-Deux-Mers south of the river. This part of the Dordogne is called the Périgord Pourpre, purple because of its red wine, though for a long time white wines have predominated. Today, approximately one third of the vineyard area is devoted to making white wines which account for roughly half the total volume of wine produced.

The Bergerac and Côtes de Bergerac appellations cover ninety communes from Saint-Michel-de-Montaigne and Minzac in the west to Baneuil and Rampieux in the east, and from Saint-Géry in the north to Eymet in the south. There are some 13,000 hectares planted with vines, roughly the same as the Médoc or Alsace and the Bergerac appellation is the largest in the south-west of France, after Bordeaux. However, it is worth remembering that in 1875, just before phylloxera struck, there were 91,000 hectares under vine.

The climate is similar to that of Bordeaux but rather more continental with less rainfall and slightly higher temperatures. At some 150 kilometres from the Atlantic, there is nevertheless some oceanic influence as evidenced by the relatively high humidity of the air with the Dordogne valley acting like a funnel for the prevailing westerlies. Rainfall can be very variable and summer storms and hail are a constant threat.

The Bergerac appellation includes the specific appellations of Montravel, Saussignac, Monbazillac, Pécharmant and Rosette and these are dealt with separately. There are some interesting pockets of "terroir" outside these specific areas, however, which are worthy of note. The Sigoulès plateau, extending as far as Eymet and Thénac, is made up of Tertiary limestone and is characterised by a group of hills intersected by streams that flow into the Dordogne or the Dropt. Issigeac to the south-east of Bergerac has its own particular terroir of sedimentary limestone giving the wines their own typicity whilst Thénac has marl and clay soils with fossilised oyster deposits, interspersed with white limestone, producing characteristically powerful wines.

AOC Bergerac, Bergerac Sec, Côtes de Bergerac

- permitted grape varieties for red and rosé wines are: Cabernet Sauvignon, Cabernet Franc, Merlot, Côt (Malbec), Fer Servadou, Mérille or Périgord. In practice, the first four named are used.
- permitted grape varieties for white wines are: Sémillon, Sauvignon, Muscadelle, Ondenc, Chenin Blanc. Ugni Blanc may be used up to 25% of the blend with at least as much Sauvignon. In practice the first three are used, occasionally with some Chenin.
- minimum planting density of 3000 vines to the hectare.
- maximum alcohol content of 13% for Bergerac and Bergerac Sec, 13.5% for red Côtes de Bergerac and 14.5% for white Côtes de Bergerac. Higher levels by special dispensation.
- basic yields of 50 hl/ha for all Côtes de Bergerac, 55 hl/ha for Bergerac Rouge and Rosé and 60 hl/ha for Bergerac Sec.
- AOC status for red Côtes de Bergerac only granted as a result of tasting after bottling.
- wines should be blended from at least two of the permitted grape varieties.

In view of the last statement, you might well be confused by the increasing number of Bergerac wines that purport to be simply Sauvignon or Merlot. With the growing popularity of these grape varieties, it is not surprising that some producers are looking to satisfy market demand by supplying 100% varietals and it has to be said that rules on labeling have been relaxed somewhat recently so that the name of the varietal can appear on the label as long as it represents at least 85% of the blend.

You will occasionally come across a Vin de Pays du Périgord, probably made from Chardonnay, or indeed a Vin de Table as at Jonc Blanc in Montravel. When I asked winemaker Franck Pascal the reason why he had chosen to market his wine as a simple vin de table, the reply was quite unexpected. Franck matures his red Montravel in a 5000 litre "foudre" and by the time he was ready to bottle, the sole bottle supplier to the Syndicat of the special embossed "In Monte Revelationem" bottles, had none left. Franck asked to bottle in standard Bordeaux bottles but this was refused. He could have kept his wine in the oak foudre till the bottles were ready but this would have changed the character of his wine.

He could have kept the wine in a holding tank but would have had to stabilize it with sulphur and this is something he chooses to avoid. So his only solution was to sell it as vin de table. The footnote to this story is that the wine proved so popular that he has continued to market subsequent vintages as table wine.

All of which goes to show that the appellation system is perhaps not as straightforward as it used to be. The old hierarchy of vin de table - vin de pays - VDQS - AOC is not so dependable any more. Within the Bergerac appellations, it is understandable to think that a Pécharmant or a Montravel, for example, will necessarily be better than a Bergerac or a Côtes de Bergerac. However, some of Bergerac's top producers are located outside the specific appellations. They must therefore devote all their skills and passion to producing a wine under the Bergerac or Côtes de Bergerac appellation which is nonetheless a classic of its kind, a flagship wine that will bear comparison with the best from Montravel or Pécharmant, or indeed many grand châteaux in Bordeaux.

MONBAZILLAC

Situation and Terroir

The Monbazillac appellation covers the communes of Monbazillac, Colombier, Pomport, Rouffignac de Sigoulès and Saint Laurent des Vignes, situated to the south of Bergerac. The vineyards are largely north-facing and their particular microclimate makes them prone to autumnal mists from the nearby river which, in conjunction with sunny afternoons, create ideal conditions for the development of botrytis cinerea or noble rot.

Geology is varied with a mixture of Agenais and Fronsadais molasse and Monbazillac and Castillon limestone. On the terraces, there are well-drained loamy soils and a little gravel with clays on the lower slopes towards the river.

History

Viticulture in the Monbazillac area probably goes back beyond the 14th century when the vineyards were the property of nobles and ecclesiastics but as they were not residents of Bergerac, they were unable to sell their wines in the town or had to pay high taxes. In the 15th century, the Bergeracois gradually took control of these vineyards and in 1495 they were officially recognised as the "Vinée Sud" and their future was assured. The export trade with Holland, which flourished in the early 18th century, meant that practically the whole production of Monbazillac was sent abroad and it rivalled the wines of Sauternes in importance. In more recent times, after the devastating frosts of 1956, low density planting and the use of mechanised harvesting combined with bad practice in the winery - excessive use of sulphur and over-chaptalisation - led the consumer to turn away from the wines of Monbazillac. Fortunately there has now been a return to harvesting by hand with at least three passes through the vines to select grapes that are affected by noble rot and great wines are again being produced by the best winemakers.

The Wines

Monbazillac is generally made from a blend of the main white varieties, Sémillon, Sauvignon Blanc and Muscadelle. The latter was widely planted back in the 18th century but now generally plays a minor role. However, there are some interesting exceptions that are worth seeking out based entirely on Sauvignon Gris, a lesser-known relation of Sauvignon Blanc, or indeed Muscadelle. The wines vary in weight but are usually sweet and honeyed, with rich candied fruit flavours and need a touch of acidity to prevent them being cloying.

AOC

- Permitted grape varieties are: Sémillon, Sauvignon, Muscadelle.
- Vines must be planted at a minimum density of 3300 vines to the hectare.
- Basic yield fixed at 30 hl/ha.
- Minimum sugar content of 221 grammes per litre of must.
- Grapes to be harvested by hand, by selective picking.
- Grapes must be over-ripe and may be affected by noble rot though not necessarily.

MONTRAVEL

Situation and Terroir

Montravel is in the far west of the Dordogne, next door to the Côtes de Castillon and comprises the communes of Bonneville, Fougueyrolles, Lamothe-Montravel, Montcaret, Montpeyroux, Montazeau, Nastringues, Ponchapt, Port-Ste-Foy, Saint-Antoine-de-Breuilh, Saint-Michel-de-Montaigne, Saint-Seurin-de-Prats, Saint-Vivien, Vélines and Saint-Méard-de-Gurçon south of the D32. It is at the eastern end of a vast plateau which extends from St. Emilion to Le Fleix and is traversed by just two streams, the Lidoire which forms the boundary between the Gironde and the Dordogne departments, and the Estrop. The vineyards are mainly south facing on soils that vary from sandy clays, often rich in iron deposits, to clay-limestone on the slopes.

History

Surrounded as it is by the appellations of Côtes de Castillon, Entre-Deux-Mers and Bordeaux-Ste-Foy, it is not surprising that Montravel has for a long time been under the jurisdiction of Bordeaux. Indeed, from 1307 to the Revolution, it belonged to the Archbishop of Bordeaux and Montravel wines were allowed free access to Bordeaux. There is evidence that winemaking was widespread from the 12th century and by the 14th century, one third of the cultivated area was given over to vines. The history of Montravel is inextricably linked to the philosopher Michel Eyquem de Montaigne, winemaker and mayor of Bordeaux. He wrote his Essays, published in 1580, in a tower which formed part of the château's defences and which fortunately escaped the disastrous fire of 1885 which destroyed the main building.

In more recent times, Montravel Rouge became the first new French appellation of the new millennium thanks to the dedication and enthusiasm of Daniel Hecquet of Château Puy-Servain and former President of the Montravel Syndicat, and Serge Dubard of Château Laulerie.

Particularities of this new appellation which came into force on November 23rd 2001 are that vines must be planted at a minimum density of 5000 to the hectare and that AOC status is only granted as a result of tasting after it has been bottled, which is extremely rare amongst French appellations.

The Wines

Montravel has long been known for its white wines. Nowadays, the dry whites have often benefited from maceration on the skins, cool fermentation and ageing on the lees, sometimes in oak, which give them a roundness and a complexity coupled with a characteristic minerality. The Côtes de Montravel and Haut-Montravel appellations are a little confusing, the only difference being the area of production. The Haut-Montravel name is restricted to 5 communes to the south and east of the river Estrop. The wines can be either moelleux (semi-sweet) or liquoreux (sweet dessert wines) at the moment but moves are afoot to clarify this situation by reserving the Côtes appellation for moelleux and Haut-Montravel for liquoreux wines.

AOC

- Permitted grape varieties are: Sémillon, Sauvignon, Muscadelle for the whites. Merlot, Cabernet Sauvignon, Cabernet Franc, Côt for the reds.
- Vines must be planted at a minimum density of 5000 to the hectare.
- Minimum sugar content of 153 grammes per litre of must for whites; minimum of 170 grammes for reds. For Côtes de Montravel and Haut-Montravel, 204 grammes minimum.
- Basic yield fixed at 58 hl/ha for dry whites, 50 hl/ha for reds, 50 hl/ha for Côtes de Montravel and Haut-Montravel.

PECHARMANT

Situation and Terroir

The Pécharmant appellation covers approved parcels in the communes of Bergerac, Creysse, Lembras and Saint Sauveur, to the north-east of the town of Bergerac on the right bank of the Dordogne. Soils are largely sands and gravels of the Périgord over iron-rich clays known as "tran". There is some Cretaceous limestone towards Lembras. The majority of the vineyards are south-facing.

History

The Pécharmant vineyards are some of the oldest in the Bergerac region, going back to the 11th and 12th centuries when they were in the hands of local gentry or the ecclesiastics of the Priory of Saint Martin and later formed the basis of the "Vinée Nord". Already in the 13th century, the wines of Pécharmant were being exported to England but often these would be sweet white wines until in the 18th century there was a demand for dark alcoholic wines and these were often made from the Fer grape and indeed were used to beef up the wines of Bordeaux.

However, the frosts of 1882, followed by the ravages of phylloxera, had destroyed the vineyards by 1883 but it is heartening to see in Féret's report of 1903, just twenty years later, the extent to which properties such as Corbiac had replanted with American rootstock. In 1943 the Rosette-Pécharmant Syndicat was set up and the two appellations were granted AOC status just after the Second World War in 1946.

The Wines

Pécharmant is generally dense and dark in colour, full-bodied with ample tannins, often matured in oak and long lasting. They are often at their best after 6 or 7 years though I do feel that they have become more approachable in recent years, partly because of vinification methods and also the balance of Merlot and Cabernets used.

AOC

*   Pécharmant must be a blend of at least three of the following grape varieties: Cabernet Franc, Cabernet Sauvignon, Côt, Merlot.
*   Planting density of at least 4000 vines to the hectare.
*   Basic yield fixed at 45 hl/ha.
*   Minimum sugar content of 180 grammes per litre of must.
*   Wines must be matured until the 1st September of the year following the harvest.

ROSETTE

Situation and Terroir

White wines only from the communes of Bergerac, Creysse, Lembras, Ginestet, Maurens and Prigonrieux, to the north and west of Bergerac itself. Close to the river, soils are Périgord sands and clay whilst further north, there are clay-limestone soils on a limestone base. From La Force to Sainte-Foy-des-Vignes, the hills form a natural amphitheatre whilst from Prigonrieux west to La Force stretches a plateau reaching 120 metres in height. East of Prigonrieux, a dry valley isolates a small plateau and the hamlets of Combrillac and Cardinolle.

History

The history of Rosette is linked very closely with that of Pécharmant, forming as they did the "Vinée Nord" back in the 13th century. The area was granted its own AOC in 1946 but then practically disappeared until the 1960s when it was revived by a winemaker returning to France from North Africa. In the 1994 edition of Féret's "Bergerac et ses Vins", only four or five producers were mentioned and still today there are only ten to fifteen enthusiasts making this semi-sweet wine.

The Wines

Light straw in colour, Rosette is a semi-sweet moelleux, floral and fruity, excellent as an aperitif or for drinking on its own at any time. There may not be many on the market but it is definitely worth seeking out. It offers pleasant easy drinking but the best examples are not without a touch of complexity. These wines are just a bit different.

AOC

- Permitted grape varieties are Sémillon, Sauvignon and Muscadelle.
- Minimum sugar content of 204 grammes per litre of must.
- Yield limited to 40 hl/ha.

SAUSSIGNAC

Situation and terroir

This area comprises the four communes of Gageac-et-Rouillac, Monestier, Saussignac and Razac-de-Saussignac, situated to the west of Monbazillac. It is essentially a plateau on the left bank of the Dordogne, intersected by the deep valleys of the Gardonnette, the Seignal and other streams. In common with Monbazillac, most of the vineyards are north-facing with a microclimate favouring the production of noble rot.

Soils are on a base of Fronsadais or Agenais molasse, often covered by boulbène, brown silty soil, or clay-limestone over Castillon limestone, often rich in iron as typified by local names such as Rouillac, La Ferrière and Ferriol.

History

Already at the beginning of the 16th century, Rabelais wrote in "Pantagruel" of the monks of Monestier who were not averse to the odd bottle of Saussignac. There is even documentary evidence that viticulture was the main occupation in the commune of Gageac-et-Rouillac back in the 11th century. In more recent times, decrees in 1956, 1967 and 1982 recognised the terroir of Saussignac by giving permission to use first, the rather wordy "Côtes de Bergerac-Côtes de Saussignac" appellation and then simply "Saussignac" for the sweet wines. From the 1990s, some of the zone's most committed winemakers, along with the local Syndicat, have fought long and hard to achieve recognition for the liquoreux wines produced, rather than the semi-sweet moelleux. On February 25th 2005, a new decree finally ratified the latest Saussignac appellation that would be reserved for dessert wines with a minimum of 17 degrees of natural sugar at harvesting with vines planted at 5000 to the hectare and a ban on all chaptalisation, regulations which are even more stringent than for Monbazillac. One of the most striking features of viticulture in Saussignac is the huge commitment to organic methods with an ever increasing number of producers being involved.

The Wines

Dry whites and reds are sold under the Bergerac or Côtes de Bergerac label. Saussignac prior to 2005 may be moelleux rather than liquoreux and in truth the semi-sweet variety does not do justice to the appellation so stick to later vintages or use this guide to seek out the best producers who have always flown the Saussignac banner.

The wines have aromas of acacia and honey with luscious fruit flavours (peach, apricot, oranges) balanced by a streak of acidity. They can last up to ten years but are delicious when young.

AOC

- Permitted grape varieties are: Sémillon, Sauvignon, Muscadelle.
- Vines must be planted at a density of 5000 to the hectare.
- Basic yield fixed at 25 hl/ha. maximum.
- Grapes to be harvested by hand and only botrytised or passerillé grapes to be used.
- Cryo-extraction is forbidden.
- Minimum sugar content of 238 grammes per litre of must.
- Chaptalisation is forbidden.

Grape Varieties

It is not surprising that the grape varieties grown in the Dordogne are more or less the same as in neighbouring Bordeaux: Merlot, Cabernet Sauvignon, Cabernet Franc and Côt (Malbec) for the reds and Sémillon, Sauvignon and Muscadelle for the whites. There is also a small amount of Sauvignon Gris which is worth seeking out and Chenin Blanc. Ondenc and Ugni Blanc are permitted in white wines but are rarely found and similar comments apply to red varieties Fer Servadou and Mérille/Périgord.

Red Varieties

Merlot

The Merlot, or Merlot Noir to give it its full name, is a major player in Bergerac accounting for 56% of the total plantings of red varieties. It is well suited to clay soils but will adapt to most terroirs. It buds and flowers early so is susceptible to late frosts and prone to "coulure". It also ripens earlier than Cabernet Sauvignon, for example, but is thin-skinned so liable to rot if the weather is wet at harvest time. It is generally seen as giving wines that are soft and fruity and useful to flesh out the sterner structure of a Cabernet Sauvignon but here in the Dordogne it often produces wines that possess firm tannins to balance the ripe fruit.

Cabernet Sauvignon

At its best in the Médoc and Graves areas of Bordeaux, the Cabernet Sauvignon plays an important but minor role in Bergerac, representing 23% of total plantings. It does well on gravelly, well-drained soils which are well-exposed, such as siliceous clays, shallow clay-limestone soils which are found throughout most of the region and gravels on the terraces as at Pécharmant and towards Lalinde. The variety produces wines which are deep-coloured and adds structure and tannins to a blend.

Cabernet Franc

The Cabernet Franc has similar qualities to Cabernet Sauvignon though they are less pronounced. It does however have the advantage of ripening earlier and is perhaps more aromatic. It is suited to clay soils, gravels, iron-rich clays such as are found in Pécharmant, and clay-limestone soils on the plateaux as in Montravel and elsewhere. Currently it accounts for 19% of the area under vines.

Malbec

Malbec or Côt plays a very minor role at just 2% of the total. Its vigour needs to be curbed by dense planting and by grafting onto low-vigour rootstock. It can add colour, aromatics and tannins to a blend.

White Varieties

Sémillon

The Sémillon grape is really at home in the Dordogne where it is well suited to the limestone and clay-gravel soils. It is the most widely planted variety and represents 64% of the total planting of white grape vines. It is a vigorous variety and must not be allowed to over-produce. It is often at its best when used in combination with Sauvignon, both in dry and sweet wines. It adds a deep golden colour, a certain fatness and roundness of flavour, ages well, is particularly susceptible to noble rot and adapts well to oak, developing a certain complexity.

Sauvignon

Sauvignon generally means Sauvignon Blanc but there is a small amount of Sauvignon Gris also planted. Plantings of Sauvignon have increased in recent years so that it now represents 27% of total white grape varieties as opposed to 18% in 1994. This is no doubt due to the global increase in the popularity of Sauvignon-based dry white wines. It is generally the first variety to be picked and is very aromatic though if picked too early can be aggressively acidic. It does well in the siliceous soils of the Rosette area and in the clay-limestone found throughout the region.

Muscadelle

Muscadelle has maintained its position as a valued though minor player in the sweet white wines of Monbazillac, Saussignac and Côtes de Bergerac moelleux, representing 9% of plantings. It adds a typical Muscat perfume to blends.

From Vine to Wine

Although the rules governing the different appellations lay down basic parameters within which winemakers must work, attitudes and methods vary a good deal from one producer to the next. Indeed, it is these differences that make for a diversity of style within the Bergerac area which is a source of great interest for the wine tourist, if a little confusing for the consumer trying to categorise Bergerac wine.

What can be said without too much fear of contradiction is that wine is made in the vineyard. Without good healthy fruit, it is not possible to make quality wine although the latest techniques in the winery mean that there should be few poor wines on the market. One of the factors relative to producing quality fruit is planting density and the latest trend is to plant at high densities. The 2001 Montravel rouge appellation required planting at 5000 vines to the hectare as a minimum and many producers, not just in Montravel, plant even closer. This density equates to planting a vine every metre with two metres between rows. What is important is the amount of fruit being produced by each vine and obviously at a planting density of 5000, each vine is being asked to produce half as much as in a vineyard planted at 2500 to the hectare, assuming a yield of, for example, 50 hl/ha. In simple terms, less quantity usually means more quality. You can still see vines planted wide and high and some producers remain convinced of the advantages of doing so. The height of the canopy is adjusted accordingly and it is easier to harvest quickly by machine. It is also less expensive in fuel as the tractor has fewer rows to negotiate and therefore, one could argue, less harmful to the environment. As we become more and more conscious of carbon footprints, it may well be that the trend will change yet again.

I have spoken to over a hundred producers during the compilation of this guide and what has been quite striking is the number of winemakers, or rather vine growers, who are certified organic or are working towards certification, most commonly with Ecocert. Something in the order of 18% fall into this category with a staggering 40% in the Saussignac area. This compares with a figure of about 1% nationwide. Remember that there is no such thing yet as an organic wine because of the use of sulphur prior to bottling. The nearest we can get is to have wine that is produced from organically grown grapes, in line with the following stipulations:

- limited yields
- aeration of the soil
- no use of synthetic chemical pesticides or herbicides
- harvesting by hand
- little or no chaptalisation or acidification
- limits on the use of sulphur dioxide
- use of indigenous yeasts
- limited fining and filtration

Some organic growers go further than this and incorporate biodynamic procedures, usually the use of decoctions made from plants such as nettles, ferns, laurel and willow. The area of biodynamism is quite fascinating but is beyond the scope of this guide. Suffice to say, whatever one's opinions regarding the use of cow's horn dung to dynamise the vineyard, the wines produced using these methods always seem outstandingly good. To try and simplify an immensely complex subject, it is a bit like homeopathic medicine. It can work but you need to believe in it. Perhaps more importantly, organic growers are more aware of environmental issues in general and are concerned about such areas as biodiversity, soil structure, product quality and consumer health.

What we must not forget is that viticulturalists are the second biggest users of agro-chemicals and that agricultural workers show the highest incidence of cancers of any group of workers. Which brings us to "la lutte raisonnée" or rational control (of pests). Some 55% of the producers in this guide professed to following these methods which basically means that instead of spraying systematically every ten days or so, as used to happen, they only spray when and where there is evidence of a problem. Those of an organic persuasion believe that "la lutte raisonnée" does not go far enough as it still puts money in the coffers of the big chemical companies, is often followed for purely economic rather than ecological reasons and acts as a salve for consciences when one should be doing far more for the environment. It is, however, a step in the right direction and I have found that many who have followed or are following "lutte raisonnée" principles, see it as a stepping stone to organic production, or at least to a method of working that respects the environment. For example, many are already using organic fertilisers, are grassing down between rows which helps prevent erosion, are treating their waste water and maintaining ditches and hedgerows.

One should not forget also that there are producers who refuse to be labelled organic or anything else, who produce excellent wine, respect the environment but reserve the right to use pesticides if it means saving their crop. In the final analysis, it is a producer's attitudes and philosophy that will guide the way he works in the vineyard, rather than simply the AOC regulations.

In the winery, advances in technology have transformed winemaking in recent years. The advent of stainless steel tanks and temperature-controlled fermentation has radically changed dry white wine production. Maceration on the skins for a few hours prior to pressing and fermentation has become standard practice and there is often a period of lees maturation afterwards. Inert gases are frequently used in the early stages to prevent oxidation. Most wineries are now equipped with pneumatic presses which are much gentler and avoid crushing the pips.

For red wine production, there is usually a cool maceration period of a few days before fermentation, again temperature-controlled. Total vatting time can be anything from a week to a month depending on the style of wine being produced. Pumping over and "pigeage" are used to extract colour and flavour and some producers make use of micro-oxygenation techniques to reduce pumping, to soften harsh tannins and to rejuvenate yeast cells. Oak barriques, usually of 225 litres, sometimes larger, are used to mature and sometimes vinify both red and white wines. The barrels are most commonly of French oak though occasionally of American, Eastern European and Russian oak. The latter is very similar to French oak but half the price. Sometimes second-hand barrels are bought from top Bordeaux châteaux and this can represent a saving of 75% on a new one which can cost up to 600 euros.

The sweet white wines of Monbazillac and Saussignac are made from grapes affected by noble rot or "botrytis cinerea", though some "passerillé" grapes may be used, i.e. grapes which have been allowed to dry on the vine. At least three passes are made through the vineyard to select the grapes which are at the correct stage of concentration. Top cuvées are often matured in oak. These sweet wines vary considerably in style, partly because of Mother Nature, partly because of decisions made in the winery. Indeed, the same can be said of all Bergerac wines. The reds can be light and fruity or powerful and long-lasting; the whites, fresh and aromatic or fuller and more complex. A whole host of factors affect the finished article from decisions regarding when to harvest to what degree of toasting to choose for the barrels. However, one pre-occupation seems to grip almost every producer and that is this notion of "terroir" and the desire to produce a wine that best reflects the "terroir" which gives it its own identity. Geology, soils, exposition, microclimate are all involved in this notion. The Syndicat de Bergerac, with the Chambre d'Agriculture de la Dordogne and ENITA de Bordeaux are to be congratulated on producing a comprehensive geological map of the whole vineyard area of Bergerac and a detailed study of the soils which allow growers to match grape varieties with the parcels of land most suitable for growing them. The various "terroirs" are mapped out in great detail. The importance of this concept of "terroir" was brought home to me when I visited Luc de Conti at Château Tour des Gendres in Ribagnac. He took me into the barrel store to taste four different barrels of Sauvignon Blanc from the 2007 vintage, all picked within a few hours of each other. They were all quite different. The wine made from grapes grown on Agenais marl had the most distinctive Sauvignon character but was probably the least good, in Luc's view. Best was that grown on Monbazillac marl which was very minerally, almost Riesling-like, and would be reserved for the top Anthologia cuvée.

Recent Vintages

2000

It was a difficult start with 45 days of rain between April and July and attendant problems of mildew and oidium, plus some losses due to coulure and millerandage, problems which fortunately affected quantity but not quality. August was dry and warm which allowed for good ripening of the grapes and after analyses at the beginning of September, the start of the harvest (le ban des vendanges) was declared for the 6th. Grapes for the dry whites were ripe, healthy and aromatic though some Sémillon was short on acidity and this would have to be compensated for in the blending. Although sugar and acidity levels were correct in the reds in mid-September, it was decided to wait a little to allow the skins (which provide anthocyans that give colour) and the pips (giving tannins which provide structure) to develop further and the harvest started on the 20th, a week later than the previous year. The weather remained clement and winemakers had the choice of picking early to bring out the fruit, or later (as late as October 18th in Pécharmant) to ensure optimum phenolic maturity. For the sweet wines, botrytisation was very slow to take effect. First pick at the start of October showed surprisingly good concentration and aromas but subsequent selection became more difficult, a lot depending on whether vineyards missed the showers and how careful the selection was. Overall, a year of paradoxes, with excellent fruit quality, reds of two distinct types, light and fruity or powerful and concentrated, fresh dry whites, some with a capacity to age well after maturation on the lees, and some complex liquoreux from the best producers.

2001

The year started off rather like 2000, damp in spring and early summer, followed by two months of dry sunny weather, though temperatures in August were not too hot which helped the development of aromatics in the grapes. It was a late harvest, starting on September 17th for the whites, the weather held, and the grapes showed a good balance of sugar and acidity. A start was made on the reds at the end of the month but the good weather was interrupted by heavy rain. There were some problems with young vines when the sudden influx of water caused the grapes to split and they had to be harvested very quickly. Similar problems occurred on parcels where soils were impermeable and drainage was poor. It was a year when the work accomplished in the vineyard in terms of pruning, leaf plucking and bunch thinning was vital in determining the quality of the crop. Wines will vary depending on whether they were harvested early or late: light in structure for early drinking or intense and aromatic, possibly quite tannic, depending on vinification. This turned out to be an exceptional year for sweet wines. Weather conditions in October were perfect with mist in the morning followed by sunny afternoons. The musts showed exceptional concentration, as high as 27 degrees potential alcohol. A great year for liquoreux to compare with 1990, 1995 and 1997.

2002

It was a damp year with an extended flowering period in June which meant that ripening would be uneven, so leaf and bunch thinning would be essential, though yields would be down anyway. The summer remained cool with a lack of sunshine, though in fact rain levels were no more than average and showers were very localised so there was great variation across the region. The harvest started in the middle of September and sugar levels were high and so was acidity, so careful blending would be necessary. The quality of the whites would depend very much on the care taken in the vineyard and the skill of the winemaker. The reds were able to take advantage of the September sun and the harvest did not finish till mid-October. The grapes showed good tannins where green harvesting had taken place and resultant wines showed a wide variety of styles, rather as in 2001. Picking for the liquoreux was completed in October; quality was generally satisfactory with some very good wines being made.

2003

It always looked as though the 2003 harvest would be exceptionally early. The winter was hard and was followed by a beautiful spring with temperatures over 30 degrees in April. The vines grew very quickly, over a metre in a week, so it was no time to get behind in the vineyard. Flowering took place in the second half of May and it is normally 110 days from then till harvest. The "ban" was declared on August 25th for the whites which showed high potential alcohol and low acid levels. Winemakers decided either to harvest straight away to preserve the grapes' fresh acidity or to wait a few days and produce wines of greater richness. For the reds, the harvest could start as early as September 1st. However, although sugar and acid levels were good, polyphenols in the skins and pips were not yet fully developed largely because their maturation depends to a large extent on differences between day and night time temperatures and this did not happen in the heatwave of 2003.

Those who waited were rewarded as the pips suddenly matured during September. Temperature control during vinification was essential in this hot year and results were very good with deep colour, high alcohol, and good structure. Some parcels that were well drained suffered from the drought. For the liquoreux, the harvest started on September 30th, potential alcohol was very high but a lot of patience was required with picking continuing into November. A hectic year for the vigneron with the harvest lasting a total of three months!

2004

A generally mild year and in spite of a little scare in mid-summer, June and September enjoyed above average temperatures. September certainly helped ripening and concentration as long as yields were kept low. The dry whites were floral and fruity with good freshness and a long finish. The reds were generally rich and complex, well-rounded with good tannic structure. Some sweet wines were very aromatic, everything depending on just when the grapes were picked.

2005

After a hard winter, early spring was wet but replenished water reserves and growth was slow and regular, unaffected by the frosts of late April. A violent hailstorm in May decimated the crop at Singleyrac on the southern plateau, otherwise the month was very warm and the vines made up for lost ground, though there were some problems with coulure in the Merlot. The summer was hot and dry and although some young plants suffered from the drought, the vineyards were healthy and there was no need to spray. From a technical point of view, tests in August showed high sugar levels, marked acidity and excellent tannin and anthocyan maturity. The good weather continued through into September and the Sauvignon was brought in from the 12th. The juice was well-balanced, intensely aromatic with a complexity ranging from exotic fruits in the ripest bunches to the more customary blackcurrant leaf where the grapes had been more sheltered from the sun. Sémillon and Muscadelle were equally successful. The reds showed excellent concentration in all areas and the hot days and cool nights helped to ripen the skins as September progressed. The harvest was able to take place calmly as the Périgord remained in the grip of an anticyclone. Intense aromas and deep colour characterised all the varieties and it was relatively easy for winemakers to adjust the extraction to suit. For the sweet wines, a lot of patience was needed as the good weather seemed to be lasting forever and botrytis was finding it hard to develop due to the lack of humidity. However, mid-October, there were several wet days and noble rot developed quite regularly, so well in fact that technically the harvest was straightforward with less sorting than is usually necessary.

2006

It was a slow gentle start as in 2005 but from the second week in May, the weather turned much wetter, mildew was a problem and as temperatures rose, there was a real spurt of growth which made for a frenetic time in the vineyard. The grapes too were evolving rapidly and the harvest was set to be almost as early as 2005. However, weather patterns in August and September did not follow the script. The second half of August was dull followed by a ten-day heat wave, and then heavy rain, all of which affected the ripening process.

When the rains stopped, there was a mad rush to get in the whites, followed immediately (sometimes the same day) by the Merlot, then Cabernet Franc and Cabernet Sauvignon in quick succession. There was already a first pick of the liquoreux and the whole of the harvesting looked set to be finished by mid-October. It was a real race against time. Overall, very variable quality in a difficult year, some decent wine but best drunk young.

2007

The spring was mild and the vines were soon in advance on previous years. However, from May onwards, things went downhill. Flowering was protracted and uneven, even within the same bunch, and this led to a similar unevenness when it came to ripening of the berries. The cool and wet summer led to a lot of leaf growth but poor ripening of the grapes. Harvesting of the whites started about September 7th with the Sauvignon coming in first. They had good varietal aromas with moderate sugar and acidity levels. The good weather throughout September came just in time and many producers decided to hang on and wait for more maturity. The Merlots were looking as though they would produce fruity wines for early drinking.

How to use this guide

Owner/Winemaker: The details are accurate at the time of going to press but there are a few properties currently on the market. Regarding telephone and fax numbers, include the 0 if you are ringing in France. If you are ringing from England, the code for France is 00 33 and you then omit the 0.

How to get there: Most of the properties are on the "Route des Vins" and will be well signposted with a red sign outside the property. Directions are usually given from the main roads out of Bergerac; the D936 to Bordeaux, D933 to Eymet, N21 to Agen or Périgueux.

Appellations: This gives you a quick indication of the range of wines produced.

Price: This is an approximate guide to price though there can be a wide range of prices from an entry-level Bergerac to a top cuvée Monbazillac.

> **Band A:** Very good value with prices starting at less than 5 euros.

> **Band B:** Average prices from 5 to 10 euros though top cuvées may be more.

> **Band C:** Generally more expensive than average but can still be good value for the quality.

Vineyard: This gives you an indication of the vineyard size and the age of the vines and although grape varieties will generally be the same, you will get an idea of any bias towards Cabernet Sauvignon, for example, or Muscadelle, or even Sauvignon Gris.

Terroir: You can check out any particularities of the all important terroir.

Viticulture/Vinification: Many of the aspects of viticulture and vinification will depend on the AOC regulations. I have tried to pick out what makes each property different from the next.

Visits: Many of the winemakers do not have the staff to man a reception area full-time. If indicated, it really is best to ring beforehand to make sure someone will be there. Most speak enough English to be able to cope with your telephone call.

History: Some of the châteaux are worth a visit just for the view and I have endeavoured to indicate any other attractions that might be of interest.

The Wines: The wines highlighted are generally wines that have been well-received by the wine press, have won awards and/or have been tasted by myself and my tasting team.

Comments: These reflect the opinions of the tasting team. Even allowing for the fact that wine is a very personal thing, the comments will give you a good indication of which are the best wines to look for.

In the U.K.: If you are flying into Bergerac, you may not be able to take many bottles back home with you so this section lists importers of Bergerac wines in the U.K. These were correct at the time of going to press but arrangements can change quite frequently.

Maps: The maps are included to show the location of the vineyards and to help you plan your route. It is recommended that you use a good road map such as the Michelin (1cm=2km). As there are a lot of producers in Monbazillac, the area has been split into East and West for your convenience, divided by the D933. In order to help with your planning, some villages have been included in the specific appellation areas although they lie just outside. So, for example, Thénac is included in Saussignac; Ribagnac in Monbazillac East; Mouleydier in Pécharmant. Properties to the south and east of the region have been grouped under the Eymet-Issigeac-Lalinde heading.

The Producers

Rosette & Pécharmant

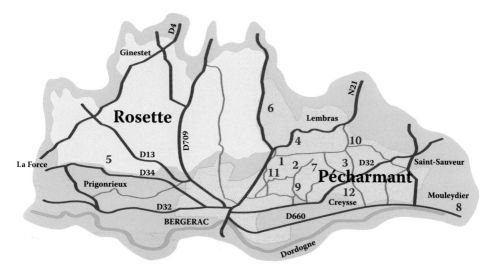

1.
*Château
Beauportail*

2.
*Château
Champarel*

3.
*Les Chemins
d'Orient*

4.
*Château
Corbiac*

5.
*Domaine de
Coutancie*

6.
*Domaine du
Grand Jaure*

7.
*Domaine du
Haut Pécharmant*

8.
*Château
Les Merles*

9.
*Château
Neyrac*

10.
*Château
Terre Vieille*

11.
*Château
la Tilleraie*

12.
*Château
de Tiregand*

Château Beauportail

Owner/Winemaker: Fabrice Feytout
Address: Route des Cabernets, 24100 Bergerac
Tel: (0)5 53 24 85 16
Fax: (0)5 53 61 28 63
Email: truffiere@beauportail.com
How to get there: From Bergerac, take the N21 towards Périgueux, after 2 km take the Pombonne road on the right and after 50m, the first right and Ch. Beauportail is 800m.
Appellations: Pécharmant, Monbazillac (Château la Truffière)
Price: Band B/C
Vineyard: The ten hectare site is planted with Merlot (50%), Cabernet Sauvignon (25%), Cabernet Franc (20%) and Malbec (5%), the oldest vines being 40 years old. Replanting is at a density of 5000 vines to the hectare.
Terroir: South and south-west facing slopes of clay and silt soils on a base that is rich in iron (tran) and silica.
Viticulture: When you visit Château Beauportail, the first thing that Fabrice Feytout does is show you his vines which are the key to his success. Most important is his systematic thinning of leaves and fruit with 50% of the bunches being sacrificed and leaf thinning taking place on both sides to ensure mature and healthy fruit. Fabrice is a great believer that wine is made in the vineyard rather than in the winery. The soils are worked until July 14th when the grass is allowed to grow between rows. Beauportail was the first property in Pécharmant to treat its waste water. Yields are low at 35 hl/ha.
Vinification: Each parcel is vinified separately with a long temperature-controlled cuvaison and manual pigeage. Micro-oxygenation is used when necessary but this process does have the effect of reducing the staying power of the wine. The Pécharmant spends 12 months in oak and the Quintessence 20 months, with stirring of the lees.
Visits: Every day from 10.30 a.m. to 7.00 p.m. It is advisable to ring Fabrice on his mobile-(0)6 08 03 13 16. French and English spoken.
History: The property dates back to the 18th century and was acquired by Fabrice in 1998. He is also proprietor at Château la Truffière in Monbazillac since 2003 and both his Pécharmant and his Monbazillac have received critical acclaim in the guide Hachette and the International Wine Challenge, culminating in the outstanding achievement of a Coup de Coeur for both the Quintessence and the Grains Nobles de la Truffière in the 2008 Hachette.
The Wines: Pécharmant Château Beauportail
Quintessence de Beauportail
Grains Nobles de la Truffière
Comments: I tasted the Quintessence 2005 on the day it was bottled. It had fresh pure fruit flavours, balanced by tannins and soft oak vanillas and was even better the following day. The Pécharmant 2005 was almost opaque with aromas of oak, spice and autumn leaves, in the mouth flavours of rich black fruits with well-integrated tannins, supple, rounded and ripe. Delicious! The Monbazillac Grains Nobles de la Truffière had a honeyed nose of almonds and coconut and lusciously rich citrus fruits in the mouth with just a hint of acidity to prevent it being cloying.
In the U.K.: Not available

Château Champarel

Owner/Winemaker: Françoise Bouché

Address: Pécharmant, 24100 Bergerac
Tel: (0)5 53 57 34 76

How to get there: As you enter Bergerac on the N21 from Périgueux, take the first little road on the left after the first traffic lights. Follow this road as far as the "Hameau de Pécharmant" sign and then turn left into a cul-de-sac, following the signs to the domain which is 1km further on.

Appellations: Pécharmant
Price: Band B
Vineyard: Six hectares in production, south-facing slopes planted with Merlot (50%), Cabernet Sauvignon (30%) and Cabernet Franc (20%). The vines are about 25 years old.

Terroir: Clay and siliceous soils on a limestone base.

Viticulture: Planted at 4000 vines to the hectare, the property falls into the "lutte raisonnée" category, though not officially. Every other row is grassed down and there is some leaf thinning and green harvesting as necessary. Yields are 45 hl/ha and harvesting is by machine.

Vinification: The grapes are de-stemmed but not crushed and cultured yeasts are used in the fermentation process which takes place in stainless steel or vitrified steel. Pumping over extracts colour and tannins and the cuvaison lasts 2 to 3 weeks. The Prestige cuvée is matured in new oak, the remainder in two-year-old barrels.

Visits: Monday to Friday, 9.00 a.m. to 12.00 a.m. and 2.00 p.m. to 5.30 p.m., weekends by appointment. It is best to ring beforehand. French and English spoken.

History: There has been a vineyard here since the 19th century and the present property was bought by the Bouchés in 1971. They then undertook a complete restructuring of the vineyard and developed the winery.

The Wines: Pécharmant Tradition
Pécharmant Prestige

Comments: The Pécharmant Prestige 2003 was one of the best tasted. Still with good depth of colour, a nose of oaky vanillas, leather, damp autumn leaves and a whiff of the bonfire, in the mouth, ripe dark berry flavours with well-integrated tannins and a long finish.

In the U.K.: Not available.

Les Chemins d'Orient

Owner/Winemaker: Régis Lansade & Robert Saleon Terras
Address: 19 Chemin du Château d'Eau, 24100 Creysse
Tel: (0)6 75 86 47 54
Fax: (0)5 53 22 08 38
Email: Regis.Lansade@wanadoo.fr
How to get there: Take the D32 St Alvère road from Bergerac, and once you are on the hilltop, after the Château de Tiregand, turn left towards Lembras. After about 2 km and a number of bends, take the Chemin du Château d'Eau (the water tower).
Appellations: Pécharmant
Price: Band C
Vineyard: Just short of 4 hectares of vines aged 15 years, Merlot (50%), Cabernet Sauvignon (30%) and Cabernet Franc (20%). One parcel is situated in the heart of the hamlet of Pécharmant, the other a kilometre away on the hill of la Germanie.
Terroir: Clay-siliceous soils with some sand.
Viticulture: High density planting of 6000 vines to the hectare, worked traditionally by ploughing between vines without using any chemical weedkillers. Thinning of the leaf canopy, disbudding, green harvesting, all these processes are done by hand. Harvesting is also done by hand and the grapes are carefully sorted, de-stemmed and transported to the tanks by conveyor belt. There is no pumping.
Vinification: The grapes are gravity fed into conical stainless steel vats containing 25 hectolitres which allow different parcels to be vinified separately. The maceration time varies depending on the amount of colour and tannins to be extracted. The tanks allow for manual pigeage and exact control of temperatures. The wine is aged for 15 to 18 months in French oak.
Visits: By arrangement. French, English and Persian spoken.
History: Régis Lansade was formerly an anaesthetist with Médecins sans Frontières in central Asia and notably in Afghanistan. He retrained as an oenologist in Bordeaux before buying this small property with Robert Saleon-Terras which he renamed, not surprisingly, Les Chemins d'Orient. In 2006, Régis and Robert were rewarded for their endeavours by being voted Winemaker of the Year in Bergerac for the 2004 Cuvée Jacques Fournot. Each year the main cuvée is given a special name and the 2004 vintage was dedicated to former friend and colleague Jacques Fournot who worked in Afghanistan in the sixties and seventies to develop agricultural techniques adapted to the Afghan people.
The Wines: Pécharmant Caravansérail
    Pécharmant Cuvée Jacques Fournot
    Pécharmant Cuvée Sikandar
Comments: These Pécharmants may not be the cheapest around but they must be some of the best. The basic cuvée is the Caravansérail but there was nothing basic about this wine. A hint of curry spices and tobacco on the nose with fresh berry fruits, the palate was well-balanced with intense dark fruit flavours, soft tannins and a lingering finish. The 2005 Sikandar took us up another notch with even denser colour, aromas that were a complex amalgam of spices, vanilla and prunes, and in the mouth, warm, rich, still youthful flavours of black fruits with notes of figs and sultanas, well-integrated tannins and a long finish.
In the U.K.: Not available.

Château Corbiac

Owner/Winemaker: Antoine Durand de Corbiac

Address: Château de Corbiac, Pécharmant, 24100 Bergerac

Tel: (0)5 53 57 20 75

Fax: (0)5 53 57 20 75

Email: corbiac@corbiac.com

How to get there: 3 km north of Bergerac on the N21, look out for the big sign for the château.

Appellations: Pécharmant

Price: Band B

Vineyard: 18 hectares on an estate of 120 hectares. The vines are 25 years old, Merlot (60%), Cabernet Sauvignon (15%), Cabernet Franc (15%) and Malbec (10%).

Terroir: Situated at the top of the Pécharmant hill, the soils are clay and limestone with flint and quartz on an iron-rich bed of clays called "tran".

Viticulture: A third of the vines are planted at 4500 to the hectare, the rest at 3500. Rows are grassed down and sheep manure is added to the soil when necessary. Yields are 45 hl/ha and the grapes are harvested late, from October 1 when slightly over-ripe, and with the property's own machines. The approach in the vineyard is very traditional.

Vinification: The press is of a traditional vertical design and vats are of stainless steel. The grapes have a five-day pre-fermentation maceration and a total cuvaison of up to five weeks for maximum extraction. The wines are matured, one third in barriques up to six years old, the remainder in stainless steel. The Château Corbiac is made from the oldest vines and one quarter is aged in oak.

Visits: Every day from 9.00 a.m. to 7.00 p.m. but it is best to ring beforehand. French and English spoken.

History: Wine has been made at Corbiac since the Middle Ages and currently Antoine Durand de Corbiac will be the fourteenth generation of his family to live and make wine at the Château de Corbiac. Already in 1864 Paul Durand de Corbiac was being honoured by Napoleon III for his modernization of the property at Corbiac. In the 1903 Féret guide, the domain was mentioned as being one of the first to have replanted using American rootstock after the ravages of phylloxera. In 1968 Antoine's parents Bruno and Thérèse took over the estate and from 1981 have commercialized their wine directly instead of working with the co-operative.

The Wines: Cadet de Corbiac
Château Corbiac

Comments: The Cadet de Corbiac should not be easily dismissed. Deep ruby in colour, blackcurrants and tobacco on the nose with soft, fresh blackcurrant fruit on the palate, uncluttered by any oak ageing. The Château Corbiac had quite an earthy nose though rich and spicy with hints of violets. Good balance between dark fruits and tannins, quite a dry finish.

In the U.K.: Wines are shipped directly to customers in the U.K.

Domaine de Coutancie

Owner/Winemaker: Nicole & Hervé Maury

Address: 24130 Prigonrieux

Tel: (0)5 53 57 52 26

Fax: (0)5 53 58 52 76

Email: coutancie@wanadoo.fr

How to get there: Take the D34 La Force road from the centre of Bergerac by the church of Notre Dame, the rue Mounet Sully, carry straight on at the roundabout, through the lights and then right towards La Force. After about 5 km. you will see a sign on the right for the Domaine de Coutancie.

Appellations: Bergerac Rouge, Sec, Rosé; Rosette

Price: Band B

Vineyard: 7 ha. of vines averaging 50 years of age, planted with Sémillon, Sauvignon and Muscadelle, Merlot, Cabernet Sauvignon and Cabernet Franc.

Terroir: Gently rolling, south facing slopes of gravely soils on an impervious iron-rich clay.

Viticulture: Speciality here is the Rosette where yields are as low as 35 hl/ha for the Cuvée Elina. The Sémillon and Muscadelle grapes are harvested when fully ripe but before the onset of noble rot. The grapes are hand-picked on two separate occasions though most of the grapes on the domain as a whole are harvested mechanically. Rows are grassed down and organic fertilisers are used.

Vinification: Fermentations are temperature-controlled. The Rosette has its fermentation stopped by chilling and by the technique of flash heating which avoid the excessive use of sulphur and the wine is then matured for 8-10 months, in oak for the Cuvée Elina.

Visits: Every day by appointment. French, English and Spanish spoken.

History: Nicole Maury is the sixth generation of winemakers on this estate, being a daughter of the Brichèse family. The domain was formerly a residence of Farmer Generals before the Revolution. It enjoys panoramic views over the Dordogne valley from the church spire of Bergerac to the Château de Saussignac. The family has been in the forefront of the promotion of the increasingly rare Rosette appellation, which is beginning to regain some of its popularity. It is often referred to as the least sweet of the sweet wines.

The Wines: Rosette, particularly the Cuvée Elina

Comments: Come here to taste the award-winning Rosette and if you're in the area on July 14th, there's a special brunch at the domain in the open air with tutored tasting of the estate's wines to accompany the local fare. The Cuvée Elina is pale straw in colour with a buttery nose of jasmine and honeysuckle with zesty orange touches that carry through onto the palate of candied fruits, a delicious sweet and sour offering and just a bit different. Equally good is the Bergerac Rouge Cuvée Spéciale Jules with its markedly spicy nose, great depth of black fruit flavours, well-structured with softening tannins on the finish and obvious staying power.

In the U.K.: Not available.

Domaine du Grand Jaure

Owner/Winemaker: Bertrand & Bernadette Baudry
Address: 16, Chemin de Jaure, 24100 Lembras
Tel: (0)5 53 57 35 65
Fax: (0)5 53 57 10 13
Email: domaine.du.grand.jaure@wanadoo.fr
How to get there: Follow the signs to the domain from the village of Lembras on the N21 north of Bergerac.
Appellations: Pécharmant, Rosette
Price: Band B
Vineyard: 15 hectares planted with Merlot (60%), Cabernet Sauvignon (30%), and Cabernet Franc (10%) for the Pécharmant, the vines being 25 years old. Plantings of Sémillon and Sauvignon in equal proportions for the Rosette are more recent.
Terroir: South-west facing slopes, with the red grapes planted on ancient gravels on top of ferrous clays called "tran". White varieties are planted on sand and gravel soils.
Viticulture: The vineyard is being replanted at 5000 vines to the hectare, the remainder being at 4000. Rows are alternately ploughed or grassed down, with some organic manure used when necessary. Leaf thinning is practised on the east or northerly side and with extensive green harvesting, yields are kept to 40-45 hl/ha. Bertrand is not part of the "lutte raisonnée" movement but describes his philosophy as "raisonnable", with minimum use of copper-based treatments.
Vinification: The Pécharmant undergoes a 2-3 day cool maceration with a temperature-controlled cuvaison of 3 to 4 weeks and pumping over twice a day. The tanks are stainless steel and enamelled steel and the wine is matured in oak of which one third is new, the Prestige cuvée for about a year. The Rosette is matured on its lees for 3 to 4 months.
Visits: Every day from 8.30 a.m. to 12.30 p.m. and 2.00 p.m. to 7.00 p.m. French and a little English spoken.
History: Wine has been made on the site for over a hundred years as testified by the entry in the 1903 edition of the Féret guide. It came into the Baudry family in 1920 with just 4 hectares planted with vines. These were added to over the years as the property passed from father to son and Georges, Bertrand's father, started bottling their wine in 1970. Bertrand and his sister are now fourth generation winemakers and have started producing Rosette again. They have received much critical acclaim and several Coups de Coeur in the Guide Hachette.
The Wines: Pécharmant Mémoire
Rosette
Comments: The Rosette is outstanding and ideal as an apéritif. Light in colour, it has a Sauvignon dominated nose with grapefruit to the fore and tropical fruits on the palate too, the fresh acidity combining perfectly with the underlying sweetness. Original and quite memorable, a great advert for the appellation. The Pécharmant Mémoire is more approachable then many, deep dense ruby in colour, a fruit-dominated nose with sweet spice and smoke too from a year in new oak, rounded and intense with good structure and no hard edges.

In the U.K: Not available.

Domaine du Haut Pécharmant

Owner/Winemaker: Didier Roches
Address: 24100 Bergerac
Tel: (0)5 53 57 29 50 **Fax:** (0)5 53 24 28 05
How to get there: As you enter Bergerac on the N21 from Périgueux, look out for a tiny road on the left signposted "Hameau de Pécharmant". Follow the signs for the Domaine.
Appellations: Pécharmant, Bergerac Rosé
Price: Band B
Vineyard: 23 hectares of vines, 40 years old on average, situated on the highest slopes of the appellation and south-facing. The vineyard is planted with Cabernet Sauvignon (30%), Cabernet Franc (30%), Merlot (30%) and Malbec (10%).
Terroir: Sands and gravel of the Périgord on a subsoil of grey and red clays with iron concretions, known locally as "tran".
Viticulture: Didier takes a "lutte raisonnée" approach to vineyard protection and has the benefit of a weather station on site. There is serious disbudding in May to reduce yields and grass is left to grow between rows from April onwards and this encourages insect predators.
Vinification: Grapes are sorted manually on a sorting table and are de-stemmed without being crushed, being transferred on a conveyor belt. There is a pre-fermentation maceration period at low temperatures to extract aromatics, followed by a long controlled fermentation and a cuvaison of up to 45 days with fermentation temperatures maintained at 25 to 30 degrees. Indigenous yeasts are used. The wines are aged for 3 years, clarified by successive rackings, fined with egg whites and bottled unfiltered.
Visits: June to September, every day from 10.00 a.m. to 12.00 a.m. and 3.00 p.m. to 7.00 p.m. Other months and Sundays by appointment. French, English, Spanish, Dutch, Flemish and German spoken.
History: In 1915, Jean Cazenille bought the Clos Peyrelevade which his son Louis sold in 1929 to buy the neighbouring Domaine du Haut Pécharmant. Louis' daughter Reine married André Roches in 1941 and the Roches family have been making wine here since that time, though, after the frosts of 1956 destroyed 80% of the vineyard, there was a period of polyculture and dairy farming until 1973 when André died and his widow decided to replant the domain with vines according to the AOC Pécharmant regulations. Ten years later, the vineyard was back to 23 hectares and shortly after Michel took over the family business in 1984, he bought back the Clos Peyrelevade adding a further 8 hectares. His son Didier took over in 1998, having run the vineyard at Château de Gueyze in Buzet for ten years.
The Wines: Pécharmant Cuvée Prestige
                   Bergerac Rosé
Comments: I have been enjoying the wines from this estate for nearly forty years since my late father-in-law first took me there in the late sixties. The family get together to do the blending and Didier assures me that they generally agree and that the proportions of the different grape varieties have stayed much the same over the years, although I do feel there has been a softening in style in recent years, no doubt due to other factors. Didier produces a number of cuvées, each with different proportions of the Pécharmant grape varieties but the one I prefer is the Cuvée Prestige where the depth of fruit and tannins is enhanced and softened by the oak ageing.
In the U.K.: Not available.

Château les Merles

Owner: GAEC des Merles

Winemaker: Joël and Alain Lajonie

Address: Les Merles, 24520 Mouleydier

Tel: (0)5 53 63 43 70

How to get there: Leave Bergerac on the D660 Sarlat road, go through Mouleydier and follow the signs, turning left in Tuilières. Tasting room is to the left and rear of the hotel as you arrive.

Price: Band A

Appellations: Bergerac, Côtes de Bergerac

Vineyard: 72 hectares planted with Merlot (60%), Cabernet (30%) and Malbec (10%) and for the whites, Sauvignon (40%), Muscadelle (30%) and Sémillon (30%). Vines are 20 to 25 years old.

Terroir: Shallow sandy siliceous soils over clay on a plateau facing south towards the Dordogne.

Viticulture: The Lajonies have a "lutte raisonnée" approach in the vineyard where plantings are at 3300 vines to the hectare. The rows are totally grassed down and leaf thinning is done by burning the lower leaves on one side in July and on the other in August. Short pruning is practised instead of green harvesting.

Vinification: Fermentation is temperature-controlled in cement vats with maturation taking place in either vat or barriques of Allier oak, 30 new barrels being purchased each year.

Visits: Monday to Friday, 9.00 a.m. to 12.00 a.m. and 3.00 p.m. to 6.00 p.m. Best to ring first. French spoken.

History: The Lajonie family has been making wine in the area for several generations and this property was acquired by Joël and Alain in 1983 with the vineyard doubling in size since then. The château is now a hotel and golf complex.

The Wines: Bergerac Rouge
Côtes de Bergerac Réserve

Comments: Both reds were equally good. The Bergerac was a fruit-driven traditional style and offered great value. It was a bright vibrant garnet colour with a freshness of red berry fruit, a hint of tobacco on the nose, and gripping tannins on the finish. The Côtes Réserve was discreetly oaked with a perfumed nose of lilies and papaya followed by lots of plum and blackberry fruit and a pleasantly dry finish.

In the U.K.: Not available.

Château Neyrac

Owner/Winemaker: Elise and Paul Bouché

Address: Pécharmant, 24100 Bergerac

Tel: (0)5 53 61 62 90

Email: chateauneyrac@hotmail.com

How to get there: From the centre of Bergerac, take the St-Alvére road and on leaving Bergerac, at the railway line, turn left and follow the signs to the property. At the end of this street, turn right and follow the signs.

Appellations: Pécharmant

Price: Band B

Vineyard: 9 ha on the southern slopes of the hill of Pécharmant, planted with Merlot (50%), Cabernet Sauvignon (32%) and Cabernet Franc (18%). The vines are ten years old.

Terroir: Siliceous clay soils.

Viticulture: The Bouchés are in the "lutte raisonnée" camp and practise disbudding and "épamprage" (the removal of unwanted shoots on the vine leg and head). Leaves are thinned on the east side and green harvesting takes place every July. Grapes are harvested by hand and machine at perfect maturity with the harvest rarely starting before the beginning of October.

Vinification: The grapes are de-stemmed and crushed on arrival at the chai and there are normally two "remontages" a day during fermentation. The wine is aged in French oak in two-year-old barrels bought in Saint Emilion. The barriques are topped up from a holding tank with a floating lid to replace the Angels' Share, the 5% lost to evaporation. The wines are fined with white of egg and bottled after a light filtration.

Visits: In July and August, every day from 10.00 a.m. to 6.00 p.m. Rest of the year, ring beforehand. French and English spoken.

History: Elise and Paul are young winemakers in their thirties who left the city in 2000 to return to their roots - Paul is the son of Françoise Bouché, winemaker at nearby Château Champarel in Pécharmant.

The Wines: Pécharmant

Comments: We tasted the 2005 which was deep and intense in colour, with aromas of spice and oaky vanillas, whilst on the palate there was an intensity of dark berry fruit, smooth and mellow with excellent balance and medium tannins.

In the U.K: Not available.

Château Terre Vieille

Owner/Winemaker: Gérôme Morand-Monteil

Address: Grateloup, 24520 St Sauveur

Tel: (0)5 53 57 35 07 **Fax:** (0)5 53 61 91 77

Email: gerome-morand-monteil@wanadoo.fr

How to get there: Leave the N21 Périgueux-Bergerac road at Pombonne, taking the country road to St Sauveur. Go straight on at the crossroads and the château is on the left.

Appellations: Pécharmant

Price: Band B

Vineyard: About ten hectares of 15 year old vines, comprising Merlot (65%), Cabernet Sauvignon (20%) and Cabernet Franc (15%).

Terroir: Iron-rich siliceous clays called "tran".

Viticulture: The vineyard is worked traditionally with hoeing of the vines, removal of shoots by hand, green harvesting and leaf plucking, all of which help to produce quality fruit. Grapes are harvested by hand and carefully sorted and de-stemmed. Yields are low.

Vinification: Temperature-controlled fermentation in stainless steel followed by maturation of at least a year in oak barriques. The three cuvées produced have different percentages of the three grape varieties. The Chevalier is unoaked, the Cros de la Sal spends 12 months in oak and the Terre Vieille 18 months in barrels, 25% of which are new, the rest one year old.

Visits: Monday to Friday, 9.00 a.m. to 12.00 a.m. and 2.00 p.m. to 6.30 p.m. French and English spoken.

History: The château was the property of the spiritualist philosopher Maine de Biran, born in 1766. He was responsible for organising the secondary school in Bergerac and the lycée there now bears his name. You can still visit his library at Grateloup. In his writings, there was already mention of the vines grown on the domain. The vineyard was mentioned in the 1903 edition of Féret and in the 1950s was acquired by the Morand-Monteil family only for the vines to be pulled up in their entirety. It was only in 1989 that Gérôme, along with his wife, decided to replant and recreate the vineyard from nothing. You can also view the collection of prehistoric flint tools and spearheads that have been excavated on the site of the vineyard.

The Wines:
    Chevalier St Sauveur
    Clos de la Sal
    Château Terre Vieille
    Cuvée Spéciale L'Ambroisie

Comments: The Château Terre Vieille 2003 was dark ruby in colour, just beginning to take on a brick red hue. It had quite an earthy nose that was spicy and oaky whilst on the palate it was rich and smooth with mellow black fruits, soft well-integrated tannins and a long finish. There is a pleasant reception area including tables and chairs in the garden where you can enjoy the wines in the sunshine.

In the U.K: Wines are shipped directly to customers in the U.K.

Château la Tilleraie

Owner/Winemaker: Bruno Fauconnier
Address: Pécharmant, 24100 Bergerac
Tel: (0)5 53 57 86 42
Fax: (0)5 53 57 86 42
Email: bruno-fauconnier@
vignobles-fauconnier.fr
How to get there: Arriving in Bergerac on
the N21 from Périgueux, take the first left
after the traffic lights, a small road
signposted "Hameau de Pécharmant" and
follow the signs to the property.
Appellations: Bergerac, Pécharmant
Price: Band B
Vineyard: 30 hectares planted with the red varieties Merlot, Cabernet Sauvignon, Cabernet Franc and Malbec, the vines being about 35 years old.
Terroir: Largely clay and limestone soils on an iron-rich subsoil called "tran" locally.
Viticulture: Every other row is grassed down with single Guyot training, retaining ten buds per vine. Planting is at 3300 to the hectare with recent plantings at 5000. Leaf thinning and green harvesting take place if necessary. Harvesting is both by hand and machine.
Vinification: The grapes are sorted and de-stalked before a temperature-controlled fermentation which lasts 15 to 21 days, with frequent pumping over. The Pécharmant is matured in Allier oak, one third new, for 15 months with racking every 3 months before fining with egg whites and limited filtration. With the red Bergerac, micro-oxygenation is sometimes used.
Visits: Open all year from 9.00 a.m. to 7.00 p.m. and there is always someone there from May to October. French, English and Spanish spoken.
History: Bruno is Belgian and first carved out a career for himself selling villas and swimming pools to the rich in Ibiza. A change of direction brought new challenges when he came to Bergerac and purchased Château la Tilleraie in 1993. He worked closely with oenologist Jean-Marc Dournel and has used his business acumen to market his wines which have achieved a string of successes.
The Wines: Château la Tilleraie Bergerac Rosé, Rouge, Pécharmant
                 Madeo Bergerac Sec, Moelleux
Comments: Quite a wide range to choose from. The Pécharmant had a spicy vanilla nose with hints of cherry fruit and leather. It was smooth textured with good balance of tannins and acidity, quite chewy with leather again on the finish. The Bergerac Rosé was soft and perfumed with a rose petal fragrance, rounded red fruit flavours and a touch of refreshing acidity.
In the U.K.: Drinks of France, tel: 0800 856 2056

Château de Tiregand

Owner: Descendants of Comtesse F. de Saint-Exupery
Winemaker: François-Xavier de Saint-Exupéry
Address: 24100 Creysse
Tel: (0)5 53 23 21 08 **Fax:** (0)5 53 22 58 49
Email: chateautiregand@club-internet.fr
How to get there: From Bergerac, head towards Sarlat. Pass the SNPE gunpowder factory. At the second set of traffic lights, go straight on until reaching the second roundabout with a boat in the middle. Take the left exit towards Pécharmant and cross the railway line. At the give way sign, turn right towards Ste Alvère on the D32 and continue for about 1.5 km until reaching the bottom of the hill. The entrance to Château de Tiregand is about 100 m. on the right.

Appellations: Bergerac Sec, Bergerac Rosé, Pécharmant
Price: Band B
Vineyard: 43 ha on the slopes of les Galinoux, Tiregand and la Montalbanie. Vines are 20-25 years old and recent plantings are at a density of 5800 to the hectare, slightly above the norm.
Terroir: Gravel and alluvial soils on clay with iron deposits, known locally as "tran".
Viticulture: Lowish yields of 45 hl/ha, with grapes picked at optimum maturity and sorted by hand, having been harvested by machine. Grapes for the "Grand Millésime" are harvested by hand on a 7 hectare site. Vineyard practices include severe pruning, green harvesting and leaf thinning to ensure healthy fruit.
Vinification: After 12 hours maceration on the skins, the white undergoes a temperature-controlled fermentation for about ten days. It is left for 6 to 8 weeks on its fine lees before bottling. The rosé is made by the saignée method, running off juice from a tank of red in the early stages of maceration. It is then vinified as for the white. The Tiregand Pécharmant is fermented in tank for 8-10 days followed by 10-15 days maceration. It spends about 12 months in oak whilst the "Grand Millésime" spends 18 months in barriques of which 50% are new.
Visits: Guided visits with tasting all year round, Monday to Saturday 9.30 a.m. to 12.00 a.m. and 2.00 p.m. to 5.30 p.m. Reservation is necessary. Price per adult: 3 euros. French, English and German are spoken.
History: This fine château dominating the right bank of the Dordogne was reputedly founded by a natural son of King Henry III of England, a certain Edward Tyrgan, in the thirteenth century. During the Hundred Years War and the Wars of Religion, it played an important rôle, being a protestant stronghold. In 1575, two Huguenot captains stole a famous trophy from the Catholics of Périgueux, namely the relics of Saint Front, patron saint of the Périgord. They were kept for a while at the Château de Tiregand but after the battle of Coutras, their guardians took flight and no doubt finding their booty rather cumbersome, promptly dumped it in the Dordogne!
Since 1826, the château has belonged to the Saint-Exupéry family, relations of Antoine de Saint-Exupéry the famous novelist whose works can be found in the tasting room.
The Wines: Château de Tiregand Bergerac Sec, Rosé de Tiregand
   Pécharmant: Château de Tiregand, Grand Millésime
Comments: The straight Château de Tiregand label offers a stylish, complex and approachable Pécharmant but don't overlook the Bergerac Sec which is very appealing with just the right balance of acidity from the Sauvignon and softness from the Sémillon.

In the U.K.: Tanners Wines Ltd., tel: 01743 234500

Monbazillac (East)

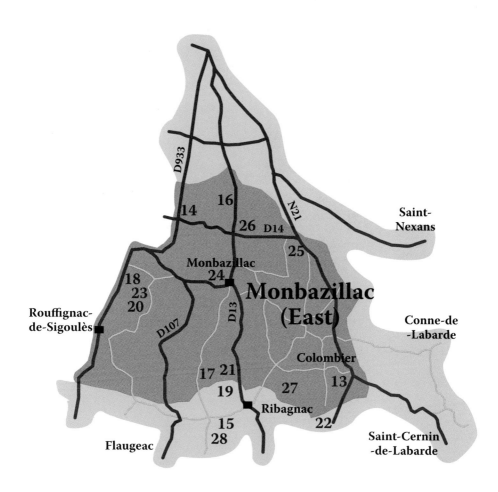

Saint-Nexans

D933

N21

14
16
26 D14
25

Monbazillac
24

Monbazillac
(East)

18
23
20

Rouffignac-
de-Sigoulès

D107

D13

Conne-de
-Labarde

Colombier

17 21
19
27
13

Ribagnac

15
28

22

Flaugeac

Saint-Cernin
-de-Labarde

13.
*Domaine de
l'Ancienne Cure*

14.
*Château
Borderie*

15.
*Château
Briand*

16.
*Château
La Brie*

17.
*Domaine
de Combet*

18.
Clos l'Envège

19.
Grande Maison

20.
*Château
Haut Bernasse*

21.
*Château
Haut Pezaud*

22.
*Château
de la Jaubertie*

23.
*Château
Kalian*

24.
*Château de
Monbazillac*

25.
*Domaine
du Petit Paris*

26.
*Château
Poulvère*

27.
*Château
La Rayre*

28.
*Château Tour
des Gendres*

Domaine de l'Ancienne Cure

Owner/Winemaker: Christian Roche
Address: 24560 Colombier
Tel: (0)5 53 58 27 90
Fax: (0)5 53 24 83 95
Email: ancienne-cure@wanadoo.fr
How to get there: The domain is situated next to the N21 Agen road, near to the junction with the road to Issigeac.
Appellations: Bergerac Rouge, Sec, Rosé, Moelleux; Monbazillac; Pécharmant
Price: Band B/C
Vineyard: 42 hectares in total of which 30 are planted with white varieties, mainly Sémillon, with Sauvignon Blanc, Sauvignon Gris and Muscadelle and 12 with red varieties, Merlot, Cabernet Sauvignon, Cabernet Franc and Malbec. Newer plantings are at 5000 vines to the hectare.
Terroir: Situated on the hill of Monbazillac on limestone interspersed with molassic sands and marl.
Viticulture: Christian is now certified organic since September 2006. Leaf thinning takes place in mid-July, on both sides for the reds, and on the eastern side for the Sauvignon. There is some green harvesting as necessary to prevent overcrowding. Yields are 45 to 50 hl/ha for the reds and 25 hl/ha for the Monbazillac.
Vinification: The dry whites are made from over-ripe grapes, cool fermented in stainless steel with some maturation in oak. The Monbazillac spends up to two years in French oak for the Cuvée Abbaye. Red grapes are carefully sorted and vinified in stainless steel and cement vats with regular pigeage. Malolactic fermentation and maturation in French oak for up to 15 months. Micro-oxygenation is used when necessary for the reds whilst still on the lees. Indigenous yeasts are normally used though Christian will use commercial yeasts if necessary.
Visits: Monday to Saturday from 9.00 a.m. to 6.00 p.m. Other times by appointment. French, German and English spoken.
History: The property is the former presbytery of the village and dates from the 13th century. It was bought by Christian's parents in the forties and Christian assumed control in 1984 but was tied to the co-operative until 1989 when he began to invest in the winery and bottling line.
The Wines: Monbazillac Cuvée Abbaye
Bergerac Rouge L'Extase
Comments: The Monbazillac Cuvée Abbaye must be about as good as it gets. Golden amber in colour, a heady nose of citrus fruits and flowers, then hugely rich and sweet botrytised fruit but always with that backdrop of citrussy acidity. L'Extase was equally good with rich damson flavours and soft dusty tannins.
In the U.K.:   Yapp Brothers, tel: 01747 860423
Les Caves de Pyrène, tel: 01483 538820
H & H Bancroft, tel: 020 7232 5450
Cellar Gascon, tel: 020 7608 0851
Waterloo Wine Co., tel: 020 7403 7967
Genesis Wines Ltd., tel: 020 7963 9060
Wine Discoveries, tel: 01580 200900

Château la Borderie

Owner: S.C.I. La Borderie

Winemaker: Vidal family

Address: 24240 Monbazillac

Tel: (0)5 53 57 00 36

Fax: (0)5 53 63 00 94

How to get there: Take the Mont-de-Marsan road from Bergerac and after 5 km turn left on the D14, then take the first drive on the left.

Appellations: Bergerac Sec, Rouge, Rosé; Côtes de Bergerac Rouge; Monbazillac

Price: Band B

Vineyard: 56 hectares with another 14 at Château Treuil de Nailhac. Sémillon, Sauvignon and Muscadelle are planted for the whites, average age 55 years. For the reds, Merlot, Cabernet Franc and Cabernet Sauvignon, average age 40 years.

Terroir: Clay-limestone soils with a northerly exposition.

Viticulture: "Lutte raisonnée" approach with vines planted at 3300 to the hectare. Every other row is ploughed or grassed down. Yields are 22-25 hl/ha for the Monbazillac and 35-40 for the red.

Vinification: The red undergoes a two week maceration before temperature-controlled fermentation in stainless steel. It is partly aged in oak barriques with racking every two months. The Monbazillac has a long fermentation of 2 to 3 months with a proportion being aged in oak and bottling after two and a half years.

Visits: Monday to Friday, 8.00 a.m. to 12.00 a.m. and 2.00 p.m. to 6.00 p.m. Weekends by appointment. French and English spoken.

History: The vineyard dates from the 14th century and there exist commercial letters dated 1663, at the time of the Wars of Religion. After the repeal of the Edict of Nantes in 1685, when the trade with Holland was at its peak, Château la Borderie was one of the 32 crus identified as the "Marques Hollandaises". Armand Vidal, proprietor of Château Treuilh de Nailhac, has developed la Borderie for over forty years.

The Wines: Monbazillac (various cuvées)

Comments: We particularly enjoyed the 1996 Monbazillac which was golden syrup in colour with a nose of toast and nuts and the flavours were all about Seville orange marmalade but it was clean and well-balanced.

In the U.K.: Not available.

Château Briand

Owner/Winemaker: Gilbert Rondonnier

Address: Les Nicots, 24240 Ribagnac
Tel: (0)5 53 58 23 50
Fax: (0)5 53 24 94 63

How to get there: From Bouniagues on the N21 Agen road, make for Ribagnac, go through the village and look for signs on the left.

Appellations: Bergerac Sec, Rouge, Rosé; Côtes de Bergerac Rouge, Moelleux
Price: Band B

Vineyard: 16 hectares planted with Merlot (60%), Cabernet Franc (20%) and Cabernet Sauvignon (20%) and for the whites, Sémillon (70%) and Sauvignon (30%). Vines are 20 to 25 years old.

Terroir: Hillside vineyard with clay-limestone soils.

Viticulture: With a "lutte raisonnée" approach to spraying, the rows are totally grassed down and leaf thinning takes place on the east or northerly side. There is green harvesting in July and August and grapes from the best parcels are reserved for the Côtes de Bergerac wines.

Vinification: All grapes are de-stemmed and the whites are macerated on the skins prior to fermentation in stainless steel tanks. The red Côtes spends 10 to 12 months in oak, 50% of which is new, and a dry white cuvée is vinified, in part, in oak barriques.

Visits: Monday to Saturday, 10.00 a.m. to 7.00 p.m. Best to ring first. French and a little English spoken.

History: The Rondonnier family has lived here for two centuries and the farmhouse dates back to the 13th century, situated not far from the Château de Bridoire. The winery is of fairly recent construction and is equipped with stainless steel tanks and barrel store.

The Wines: Bergerac Sec élevé en fût
                  Côtes de Bergerac Cuvée Zen
                  Côtes de Bergerac Cuvée Nathalie moelleux

Comments: The Cuvée Zen was the pick here with its complexity of aromas - smoke, vanilla, tobacco, black fruits - and a more fruit-driven style with soft tannins and a touch more alcohol in evidence. Semi-sweet moelleux are not everyone's cup of tea but if you like pineapples, do try the Cuvée Nathalie. Already there was pineapple on the nose, with a hint of celery, but in the mouth it was pure pineapple chunks!

In the U.K.: Not available.

Château la Brie

Owner: Lycée d'Enseignement général technologique et agricole
Winemaker: Thomas Caillaud
Address: Domaine de la Brie, 24240 Monbazillac
Tel: (0)5 53 74 42 46 **Fax:** (0)5 53 58 24 08
Email: expl.lpa.bergerac@educagri.fr
How to get there: Situated on the D13 road to Monbazillac before you arrive at the village and just before the crossroads.

Appellations: Monbazillac; Bergerac Rouge, Sec, Rosé; Côtes de Bergerac Moelleux
Price: Band B
Vineyard: On the slopes south of Bergerac, the property extends to 55 hectares altogether on three sites, La Sabatière and Lavaud in addition to La Brie. 37 ha are planted with white varieties, the majority Sémillon with some Sauvignon and a little Muscadelle. For the reds, mainly Merlot with Cabernet Sauvignon, Malbec and Cabernet Franc.
Terroir: Soils and sub-soils are clay-limestone.
Viticulture: Vines are planted at up to 4500 to the hectare for low vines and high-trained vines at 2400-2600 to the hectare. The rows are grassed down except under the vines. Single and double Guyot pruning is practised and yields are kept at a sensible level, from 27hl/ha for the Monbazillac to 66 for the Bergerac Sec. The students at the college are involved in all stages of production from the vineyard through to the marketing. Qualenvi certified.
Vinification: As the college is preparing the winemakers of the future, they have access to the latest technology and techniques such as micro-oxygenation for the reds and cryoextraction for the Monbazillac. The dry whites enjoy a maceration on the skins for just 6 to 8 hours and some follow up with fermentation and ageing in barriques with regular lees stirring. Wines are racked, fined and filtered with care and are kept in stainless steel under nitrogen until bottling.
Visits: Shop open from Monday to Friday, 10.00 a.m. to 12.00 a.m. and 1.30 p.m. to 6.00 p.m. and on Saturdays from May to September. Winery and vineyard can be visited by arrangement. French and English spoken.
History: The story of the Domaine de la Brie is closely linked to a wealthy protestant family called Eyma. After the Wars of Religion and the revocation of the Edict of Nantes, many Protestants fled to Holland and a considerable trade with the Low Countries followed with 32 of the best domains, including Château la Brie, becoming known as the "Marques Hollandaises". In 1962 the domain was purchased from Jean Eyma by the Département de la Dordogne and was originally administered by the Cave de Monbazillac until the opening of the Lycée in 1984. The Co-operative continued to vinify the wines until 1994 when the teaching winery was built. The college undertook the renovation of the façade in the style of the 18th century. Their wines have won innumerable awards over the years.
The Wines: Monbazillac
   Bergerac Rouge Cuvée Plénitude
   Bergerac Sec, Bergerac Rosé
Comments: I would definitely pick out two of the reds here. The Bergerac Prestige 2003 was drinking really well with smoke and oaky vanillas on the nose and rounded flavours of plummy fruit, soft tannins and a hint of dryness on the finish. The Plénitude had greater depth of flavour but was also well-balanced with well-integrated tannins and soft blackberry fruit.
In the U.K: Jascot's Wine Merchants, London, tel: 020 8965 2000

Domaine de Combet

Owner: Alexis family

Winemaker: Daniel Duperret

Address: 24240 Monbazillac

Tel: (0)6 85 33 50 57

Fax: (0)5 53 58 33 47

Email: earldecombet@wanadoo.fr

How to get there: From the Monbazillac plateau, take the road towards Sadillac/Lauzun. Turn left after the hamlet of Combet.

Appellations: Bergerac Rouge, Sec, Rosé; Monbazillac

Price: Band B

Vineyard: 30 hectares planted with mainly Sémillon for the whites but with Muscadelle, Sauvignon Blanc and interestingly, Sauvignon Gris. The red varieties comprise Merlot, Cabernet Franc and Cabernet Sauvignon. The red grape vines are 24 years old and the white varieties 32 years.

Terroir: Boulbène and clay-limestone on flinty limestone base.

Viticulture: "Lutte raisonnée" approach with spraying only when necessary. The domain holds a "Qualenvi" certification which guarantees service, quality and environmental reliability. Planting density has been increased to 4000 vines per hectare with some grassing down depending on the vigour of the vines. Any fertiliser used is organic and leaf thinning is carried out by hand as is harvesting for the whites.

Vinification: The Monbazillac is vinified in concrete vats with a third in oak barriques. Stainless steel and epoxy-lined steel vats are also used. The press is pneumatic and commercial yeasts are used. Interestingly the Monbazillac Exception is practically pure Sauvignon Gris which is most unusual. The Monbazillac is aged for 18 months in oak with a further 2 years in bottle.

Visits: Monday to Friday, 9.00 a.m. to 12.00 a.m. and 2.00 p.m. to 6.00 p.m. Weekends by arrangement. French and English spoken.

History: A family property which began to specialise in viticulture in the sixties. Daniel is something of an expert in "sweet fruits" having come to Monbazillac from working in the "Pruneaux d'Agen" area. He helped to form the co-operative in Monbazillac.

The Wines: Monbazillac
Monbazillac L'Exception

Comments: The Cuvée L'Exception is made from Sauvignon Gris and is a revelation of what this grape variety can produce: delicious sweet citrus flavours with a hint of pineapple and honey and melon on the finish with just a hint of acidity. The Monbazillac Fûts de Chêne was no slouch either. In fact, if anything, it was slightly better balanced with a pleasant streak of acidity to set against the honeyed citrus fruit and cinder toffee palate. Great complexity and concentration after eighteen months in oak. Definitely in the top flight of Monbazillacs.

In the U.K.: Not available.

Clos L'Envège - Julien de Savignac

Owner/Winemaker: Julien de Savignac
Company
Address: Les Tabardines, 24240
Monbazillac/ Also shop at Ave. de la
Libération, Le Bugue
Tel: (0)5 53 07 10 31
Fax: (0)5 53 07 16 41
Email: julien.de.savignac@wanadoo.fr
How to get there: On the D933 Bergerac to
Marmande road.
Appellations: Monbazillac; Bergerac Rouge,
Sec, Rosé; Rosette; Vin de Pays du Périgord

Price: Band A/B
Vineyard: Clos l'Envège is 8 hectares planted with Sémillon, Sauvignon and Muscadelle, aged about 20 years old. There is a small amount of recently planted Merlot and Cabernets.
Terroir: Heavy clay and chalk soils on south-west facing slopes.
Viticulture: Vines are planted at 5000 to the hectare and every other row is ploughed or grassed down. A "lutte raisonnée" approach is adopted and harvesting is by machine except of course for the Monbazillac where yields are as low as 10 hl/ha. As a wine merchant and négociant, Julien de Savignac also works closely with many of the top châteaux, buying in from selected parcels.
Vinification: The harvest takes place early morning to preserve freshness and the whites are macerated 72 hours, the rosé for 40 hours. They are then fermented at low temperatures in stainless steel. C.I.V.R.B. oenologist Pierre Guérin assists with the blending. The Monbazillac enjoys an 18 month fermentation in new French oak.
Visits: By arrangement for the winery at Clos l'Envège, from Easter to the end of September. The shops at Le Bugue, Périgueux (rue Taillefer) and Sarlat (Place Pasteur) are open during normal shop hours. The staff are very knowledgeable and I would particularly recommend the shop at Le Bugue if you are short of time. There is an excellent range and the prices are the same as you would pay at the cellar door. French, English and Spanish spoken.
History: Julien de Savignac specializes in marketing wines from the Bergerac region under their own label. Sourcing of high quality fruit allied to the skills of blending and ageing have resulted in an impressive list of award-winning wines. They purchased Clos l'Envège from Château Haut Bernasse and invested five million francs in developing the winery in Monbazillac including state-of-the-art equipment, a storage cellar and shop.
The Wines: Bergerac Rouge "Magis"
Bergerac Sec Cuvée Lisa
Vin de Pays du Périgord Chardonnay
Monbazillac Clos l'Envège
Comments: A Chardonnay from the Dordogne is something of a rarity and the vin de pays is certainly worth trying, sourced as it is from a parcel at la Jaubertie, with its floral nose and tropical fruit flavours. The Magis 2002 was deep damson in colour, still youthful with ripe blackcurrant fruit and mellow tannins and a dryish finish. The Clos l'Envège Monbazillac was rich, honeyed and well-balanced.
In the U.K: Not available.

Grande Maison

Owner/Winemaker: Thierry Déprés
Address: 24240 Monbazillac
Tel: (0)5 53 58 26 17
Fax: (0)5 53 24 97 36
Email: thierry.despres@free.fr
How to get there: From the church in Monbazillac, follow the signs to the property.
Appellations: Bergerac, Monbazillac
Price: Band B/C
Vineyard: 13 hectares mostly devoted to white wine production with Sémillon (60%), Sauvignon (30%) and Muscadelle (10%) being planted, average age 15 years. For the red, Merlot (80%) and Cabernet (20%).

Terroir: South-facing slopes on the hill of Monbazillac, clay-limestone soils and very stony, one parcel being called "les Cailloux".

Viticulture: Thierry has been at the forefront of organic winemaking for twenty years and became biodynamic in 1997. It is fascinating to talk to him about biodynamism which is less a technique in the vineyard, more a way of life. Perhaps the best analogy, and certainly one of the easier ones to understand, is to compare it with homeopathic medicine as opposed to conventional medicine. Thierry prunes the vines according to the lunar calendar and prepares herbal decoctions based on nettle, rat's tail, ferns and yarrow. Whatever you think of biodynamism, the results are often impressive and some of Thierry's top cuvées are quite stunning.

Vinification: Grapes are harvested by hand and fermentation is temperature-controlled with maturation taking place in oak barriques, mostly new. Cryoextraction has been used with the Monbazillac, as at Château d'Yquem in Sauternes, a method of freeze concentration whereby only the richest juice and aromas are extracted from the ripest berries.

Visits: Monday to Friday from 9.00 a.m. to 12.30 p.m. and 1.30 p.m. to 7.00 p.m. Best to ring first.

History: Former stronghold built by the English in 1290 on tenth century foundations, the Château and vineyard were in a deplorable state in 1990 when they were acquired by Thierry Déprés. They were quickly put to rights and the first vintage was produced in 1991. Many distinctions have followed with five medals in two years in the International Wine Challenge and five stars in the Robert Parker guide.

The Wines: Monbazillac Cuvée des Monstres
          Monbazillac Cuvée Exotique

Comments: The Cuvée Exotique was deep lemon in colour and remarkable for its freshness and purity of flavour, pineapple and grapefruit, tropical fruits but no heaviness and a zingy lemon acidity. Ideal as an apéritif or with fruit desserts. The Cuvée des Monstres lived up to its name, almost amber in colour, rich and honeyed with an almost oily texture but still with clean flavours of fruit and saffron, and great length. Top wines of the appellation and remember these are biodynamic.

In the U.K.: Vinceremos, tel: 0113-2440002

Château Haut Bernasse

Owner: Guy Villette
Winemaker: Sebastien Dieuaide/Thierry Toffano
Address: 24240 Monbazillac
Tel: (0)5 53 58 36 22
Fax: (0)5 53 61 26 40
Email: contact@haut-bernasse.com
How to get there: From Bergerac, take the Eymet road, pass the Monbazillac Co-operative and at the top of the hill, turn left at Malfourat, pass the Tour des Vents restaurant and turn right. Haut-Bernasse is in 500m.
Appellations: Bergerac Rouge, Sec; Côtes de Bergerac; Monbazillac
Price: Band B/C
Vineyard: 15 hectares of which 12 are planted with white varieties, namely Sémillon (70%), Sauvignon (20%) and Muscadelle (10%). The rest is made up of 80% Merlot and 10% of each Cabernet. Red grape vines average 25 years old but for the whites, up to 90 years, planted at 5000 vines to the hectare.
Terroir: Clay-limestone molasse.
Viticulture: Generally every other row is grassed down depending on the vigour of the vines. Gobelet training is used in some parcels for the Monbazillac. Leaf thinning takes place on the north and east sides and severe pruning in the spring obviates the need for green harvesting later on. Yields are down to 17 hl/ha for the Monbazillac.
Vinification: An old vertical press dating from 1910 is still in use. Fermentation is temperature-controlled and vinification is in barriques of Allier oak. Indigenous yeasts are used. The dry white is matured on its lees for nine months with regular stirring. The Monbazillac remains in barrel for two years.
Visits: Monday to Friday, 9.00 a.m. to 12.00 a.m. and 2.00 p.m. to 6.00 p.m. Weekend by arrangement. French, English and a little Spanish spoken.
History: Formerly belonging to the Bouissy family, the property was bought by Jacques Blais in 1971. He replanted almost all the vineyard and his uncompromising approach to producing quality wines did much to bring the appellation back into the public eye, and brought him the title of "Winemaker of the Year" in 1991. The domain was acquired by Guy Villette in 2002 and considerable investment has continued the pursuit of the highest quality. A long list of medals for both the Monbazillac and the Côtes de Bergerac Rouge attests to this fact.
The Wines: Monbazillac
Côtes de Bergerac Rouge
Bergerac Sec
Comments: The red Côtes de Bergerac is deep in colour with a smoky slightly burnt nose and good extract of dark fruits complemented by tannins that are beginning to soften. There are hints of spice, pepper and liquorice and a persistent finish. The Monbazillac 2001 is marked by its bright fruit and acidity which feel almost spritzy on the tongue, a complex mix of saffron, citrus and crème brûlée with a long finish.

In the U.K.: O.W.Loeb, London, tel: 0207 234 0385

Château du Haut Pezaud

Owner/Winemaker: Christine Borgers
Address: 24240 Monbazillac
Tel: (0)5 53 73 01 02
Fax: (0)5 53 61 35 31
Email: cborgers@wanadoo.fr
How to get there: Go past the Château de Monbazillac as far as the church then take the second road on the right, following the sign for the domain. It is the first house on the left after about 1.5 km.

Appellations: Bergerac Rouge, Sec, Rosé; Côtes de Bergerac Moelleux; Monbazillac; Méthode Traditionnelle

Price: Band B

Vineyard: A hilltop site of ten hectares of which seven are devoted to Monbazillac and planted with Sémillon (90%), Sauvignon Gris (5%) and Muscadelle (5%). The remainder are planted with Merlot (60%), Cabernet Franc (20%) and Cabernet Sauvignon (20%). The red grape vines are just 10 years old now but the white varieties 50 to 60 years old.

Terroir: The vineyard is situated on a plateau with soils which are clayey silt and clay-limestone.

Viticulture: Christine Borgers is in the "lutte raisonnée" camp. Every other row is grassed down and vines are planted at 5000 to the hectare. Leaf thinning is done by hand in the older vines. Green harvesting is practised for the Merlot which can be very productive but is not needed for the Monbazillac. Yields are at 55 hl/ha for the reds and 27 or less for the Monbazillac. Christine uses commercial yeasts and works closely with C.I.V.R.B. oenologist Pierre Guérin to choose the most suitable yeast for each vintage and cuvée. Harvesting is by hand.

Vinification: Fermentation takes place in tank or in barrique depending on the cuvée and the reds undergo a pre-fermentation maceration followed by pumping over twice a day during fermentation which is temperature-controlled. Part of the production is aged in oak for 8 to 12 months, a third of it new. The dry white is aged on the fine lees.

Visits: All year from 1.00 p.m. to 7.00 p.m. and in July and August from 10.00 a.m. to 7.00 p.m. Alfresco lunches are organised during the summer with a guided visit and walk in the vineyard. Contact for further details. Languages spoken are French, Dutch and a little English.

History: When her parents settled in the Dordogne some twenty years ago, Christine Borgers began her love affair with the region and its wines. She left her job as an accountant in Belgium and retrained at the Institut Oenologique in Bordeaux before buying the property at Les Pezauds, giving it a name, and starting to produce and bottle her own wines - the previous owner had sold his grapes to the co-operative. Gold medals have followed for both the Monbazillac and the Bergerac Rouge.

The Wines: Monbazillac Révélation
                   Bergerac Rouge Clair de la Roche

Comments: The Bergerac Rouge Clair de la Roche belied its label which looked a bit brash. It had blackcurrant fruit on the nose and in the mouth, was still youthful in colour and fresh and flavoursome. The Château Haut Pezaud oaked red had fruit and spice on the nose, the oak was discreet, it was vigorous and brambly with medium tannins and a slight metallic edge. The various Monbazillacs are relatively light in style with honeyed citrus fruits and a good balance between sweetness and acidity.

In the U.K.: Not available

Château de la Jaubertie

Owner: Ryman S.A.
Winemaker: Hugh Ryman and François Bacco (maître de chai).
Address: 24560 Colombier
Tel: (0)5 53 58 32 11
Fax: (0)5 53 57 46 22
Email: jaubertie@wanadoo.fr
How to get there: 11 km south of Bergerac just off the N21 Agen road.
Appellations: Bergerac Sec, Rouge, Rosé
Price: Band B
Vineyard: 50 hectares planted with Sauvignon (60%), Sémillon (35%), Muscadelle (5%) and 3.3 ha of Chardonnay. For the reds, Merlot (50%), Cabernet Sauvignon (35%), Malbec (7.5%) and Cabernet Franc (7.5%). Vines are 15 to 20 years old.
Terroir: Clay-limestone plateau some 170 metres above the valley of the Dordogne, protected from south-westerlies by a screen of trees. Vines for reds planted on the plateau with whites on the surrounding slopes.
Viticulture: Organic on the lower slopes since 2005 with certification due in 2009. In 2000 the vineyard was restructured in order to bring planting densities for the reds up to 5000 vines per hectare. The whites will eventually be at 4500 to the hectare.
Vinification: For the whites, the grapes are harvested at night to avoid oxidation. They are left on the skins for 24 hours, then fermented at low temperature with maceration on the lees. There is some oak maturation. For the reds, a cool maceration of ten days, with a percentage being aged for ten months in oak. The Cuvées Mirabelle benefit from more prolonged barrel ageing, eight months for the white in American oak and 14-16 months for the red in French oak barriques.
Visits: Monday to Friday, 9.00 a.m. to 12.00 a.m. and 2.00 p.m. to 5.00 p.m. French and English spoken.
History: The impressive Château dates from the 16th century when it was built by a nobleman for his mistress. It is said that Henri IV stayed there with his mistress Gabrielle d'Estrée and used it as a hunting lodge. A later owner, the doctor Léo Beylet, was sent paintings and parquet flooring from the Château de Rambouillet by Marie Antoinette as a thank you for his services. These can still be seen today. The Château was bought by the Rymans in 1973 as chronicled in Jeremy Josephs' "A Château in the Dordogne".
The Wines: Cuvée Tradition: Château de la Jaubertie blanc, rosé, rouge
Cuvée Mirabelle: Château de la Jaubertie blanc, rouge
Monbazillac
Vin de Pays du Périgord Chardonnay
Comments: The Rymans led the charge of Brits to the Dordogne back in the seventies and their wines are still up there with the best. I would single out the Bergerac Sec as being one of the best examples of this style of wine, pale in colour with a fresh peachy nose leading on to a palate of zingy grapefruit but with a touch of softness, great balance between the fruit and refreshing Sauvignon acidity.

In the U.K.: Charles Hawkins, tel: 01572 823030

Château Kalian

Owner: Griaud family
Winemaker: Kilian Griaud
Address: Bernasse, 24240 Monbazillac
Tel: (0)5 53 24 98 34
Fax: (0)5 53 24 98 34
Email: kalian.griaud@wanadoo.fr
How to get there: From Bergerac take the D933 Eymet
road for about 6 km before turning left at the Moulin de
Malfourat. Pass the Tour des Vents restaurant and turn right
at the Stop sign. Follow the signs for the property.
Appellations: Bergerac Rouge, Monbazillac
Price: Band B
Vineyard: 10 hectares, the majority planted with white varieties, Sémillon (80%), Muscadelle (17%) and Sauvignon (3%), aged up to 45 years. For the red, a slightly unusual Cabernet Franc (44%), Cabernet Sauvignon (43%) and Merlot (13%) averaging 20 years of age. Altitude is 130-180 m.
Terroir: The majority is on clay-limestone soils with one hectare at "L'Envège" of clay on limestone molasse best suited to white wines.
Viticulture: "Lutte raisonnée" approach with minimum spraying from April to August after checks on pests and diseases. Preventative methods used to achieve a healthy vineyard including grassing down and ploughing, a studied use of fertilisers, manual leaf thinning and disbudding, and maintenance of adjacent hedgerows and ditches, basically methods which respect the environment and ecosystems.
Vinification: No chaptalisation is practised. Grapes for the Bergerac Rouge are harvested by hand at the beginning of October, de-stemmed and crushed before being gravity fed into tanks. A cool 2-3 day maceration is followed by a fermentation controlled at 24-27 degrees with regular remontages and/or pigeages. Having gone through malolactic fermentation in tank, the wine spends a year in French oak of which 25% is new. Grapes for the Monbazillac are gathered on 3 to 5 passes through the vineyard to select those affected by noble rot. They are gently pressed and the juices kept separately depending on provenance and date of picking. They are clarified at 8 deg. and fermentation is stopped when the sugar/alcohol balance is judged correct by lowering the temperature and stabilising with sulphur dioxide. Aged up to 2 years in French oak.
Visits: Every day from 9.00 a.m. to 7.00 p.m. By arrangement for groups over 8. French and English spoken.
History: Anne and Alain Griaud fell in love with the property and its 5 hectares of vines in 1992. It was renamed Château Kalian after their children Katell and Kilian. The holding has been added to since then and Kilian took over from his parents in 2007, having qualified in viticulture and oenology.
The Wines: Bergerac Rouge
                  Monbazillac
Comments: The Bergerac Rouge had warm and spicy aromas reminiscent of hot cross buns with blackcurrant fruit prevalent throughout, rich but fresh with discreet tannins. The Monbazillac had a pronounced nose of honey, pink grapefruit and coconut with rich butterscotch fruit but not overly sweet or heavy. Quite delicious!
In the U.K.: Not available.

Château de Monbazillac

Owner: Cave Coopérative de Monbazillac
Winemaker: SCEA Château de Monbazillac
Address: Route de Mont de Marsan, 24240
Monbazillac
Tel: (0)5 53 63 65 00
Fax: (0)5 53 63 65 09
Email: cavedemonbazillac@dial.oleane.com
How to get there: Monbazillac is about 10 km
south of Bergerac. The Château is on the left as you
climb the D13 towards the village. The Coopérative
is on the D933 south of Bergerac.
Appellations: Monbazillac
Price: Band B
Vineyard: About 30 ha. of vines which are on average 22 years old. Grape varieties are Sémillon (over 22 hectares), Muscadelle and Sauvignon.
Terroir: Clay-limestone soils.
Viticulture: Planted at 5000 vines to the hectare, the soil is hoed/ploughed beneath and between rows with some grassing down according to the vigour of the vines. The grapes are left on the vines until affected by noble rot and are harvested by hand.
Vinification: After passing through the pneumatic press, the grape juice is fermented in barriques and the wine is matured for a further 12 to 14 months in oak, which is renewed every three years.
Visits: The Château de Monbazillac is one of the showpieces of the Dordogne. The site is open from April to October. French and English are spoken. The Co-operative can be visited in July and August.
History: The Château is classified as a historical monument and dates from the 16th century, being an architectural blend of a Middle Ages defensive style and the first signs of Renaissance art. The terrace enjoys an extraordinary view over the Dordogne valley and a sea of vines. The Château survived the Wars of Religion and the Revolution and in 1962 was bought by the Cave Coopérative which was founded in 1940. Over the years, it has been in the forefront of commercial and technological developments in the area. As well as the Château de Monbazillac, the Coopérative counts a number of well-known names in its portfolio, including Château Septy, Château Le Touron and La Renaudie in Pécharmant.
The Wines: Château Monbazillac
                Château Septy
Comments: The Château Monbazillac 2002 was golden in colour with slightly musty burnt orange aromas, clean crystallised lemon fruit flavours, sweet but not cloying, and a long finish.
In the U.K.: Although Château Monbazillac is not available in the U.K., other wines from the Co-operative can be obtained.
            Corney & Barrow Ltd., tel: 020 7265 2450
            Waverley TBS Ltd., tel: 0131 528 1500
            Tanners Wines Ltd., tel: 01743 234 500
            El Vino Co. Ltd., tel: 020 7353 5384
            S.H.Jones & Co. Ltd., tel: 01295 251177

Domaine du Petit Paris

Owner/Winemaker: Patrick and Bénédicte Geneste
Address: 24240 Monbazillac
Tel: (0)5 53 58 30 41
Fax: (0)5 53 58 35 63
Email: petit-paris@wanadoo.fr
How to get there: Take the N21 out of Bergerac past the airport and take the first right turn. Petit Paris is down the left fork just after the junction.
Appellations: Bergerac Sec, Rouge, Rosé; Côtes de Bergerac Rouge, Moelleux; Monbazillac
Price: Band B/C
Vineyard: 30 hectares planted with red varieties Merlot (60%), Cabernet Sauvignon (30%), Cabernet Franc (8%) and Malbec (2%). For the whites, 85% Sémillon with the rest split between Sauvignon and Muscadelle. The red varieties are 30 years old on average but the whites much older with some Sémillon and Muscadelle being 110 years old.
Terroir: Clay-limestone soils.
Viticulture: The Genestes work with a technician on a "lutte raisonnée" approach to spraying. Every other row is grassed down and leaf thinning is done by machine and also by hand for the Muscadelle. Green harvesting is often necessary with the Merlot and was particularly important in 2006. Yields are kept low, down to 5 to 15 hl/ha for the Monbazillac.
Vinification: Stainless steel and cement vats are used, the latter being particularly suitable for lees maturation as they are less susceptible to atmospheric pressure. Pumping is avoided by using conveyor belts to move the grapes. "Délestage" is used with the reds to provide quick extraction. A range of oak barrels is used to mature the top reds and the Monbazillac. American oak seems well suited to ripe Cabernet Sauvignon, French oak is used for the Monbazillac and a mixture of American and Russian oak for some of the top red cuvées.
Visits: Every day from 9.00 a.m. to 12.00 a.m. and 2.00 p.m. to 6.00 p.m. French and English spoken.
History: Patrick Geneste is the fourth generation of his family to make wine at the domain. It was already mentioned in the 1903 Féret and under Jean Geneste was known for the impeccable maintenance of its vines. All the production is now bottled at the property.
The Wines: Côtes de Bergerac Rouge
                Monbazillac Grains Nobles
Comments: The red Côtes 2003 was dark and dense in colour with a complex nose of charring, blackcurrant and liquorice. In the mouth, there was evidence of rich black fruits again with robust tannins on the finish and a suggestion that this would continue to improve for a year or two yet. The Monbazillac Grains Nobles brought back childhood memories with its pronounced nose of Airfix glue whilst on the palate, it had rich and complex honey and pineapple flavours with an oily texture.

In the U.K.: Not available.

Château Poulvère

Owner/Winemaker: Borderie family

Address: 24240 Monbazillac

Tel: (0)5 53 58 30 25

Fax: (0)5 53 58 35 87

Email: francis.borderie@poulvere.com

CHATEAU POULVERE 2006

How to get there: Leave Bergerac on the N21 Agen road, turn right on the D14 and the property is on the right just before the junction with the D13.

Price: Band A/B

Appellations: Bergerac, Côtes de Bergerac, Pécharmant, Monbazillac

Vineyard: A large estate of 105 hectares planted with Sémillon (50%), Sauvignon (25%) and Muscadelle (25%) and for the reds, Merlot (50%), Cabernet Franc (25%) and Cabernet Sauvignon (25%). The vines are 35 to 40 years old on average.

Terroir: Clay-limestone soils for the Monbazillac with a mixture of sand, silt and clay for the Bergerac and Périgord sands and gravel in the parcel at Pécharmant.

Viticulture: Of the "lutte raisonnée" persuasion, the Borderies grass down every other row and use organic fertilizers when necessary. Planting has been at 3300 vines to the hectare with recent plantings at 4000. Harvest is by machine except for the Monbazillac of course when grapes at least 80% botrytised are picked on 2 or 3 passes.

Vinification: A variety of vats are used - stainless steel, cement, glass fibre and enameled steel. The reds are fermented at 26 degrees with remontages twice a day and a total vatting time of a month for the Pécharmant and 3 weeks for the Bergerac. The best Monbazillacs are fermented in oak for 7 to 8 weeks and then matured for up to 15 months in barriques of either French or Eastern European oak.

Visits: Monday to Saturday, 9.00 a.m. to 12.00 a.m. and 2.00 p.m. to 6.00 p.m. French and English spoken.

History: Four generations of the Borderie family have made wine here, the estate formerly belonging to the Château de Monbazillac. It was owned by a bourgeois family from Bergerac till the 1940s when it passed to a Bordeaux négociant and Jean-Gaston Borderie was the chef de culture. The family bought the property in 1977.

The Wines: Various cuvées of Monbazillac
Pécharmant Les Grangettes selon Gaston

Comments: The Monbazillac Damien was the winner here with a rich texture, a medley of tropical fruit flavours, grapefruit and pineapple, clean tasting and not too sweet or heavy.

In the U.K.: Not available.

Château la Rayre

Owner/Winemaker: Vincent Vesselle

Address: 24560 Colombier

Tel: (0)5 53 58 32 17

Fax: (0)5 53 24 55 58

Email: Vincent.vesselle@wanadoo.fr

How to get there: Take the N21 Agen road out of Bergerac and after about 4km there is a double junction on the right. Take the left-hand fork through Labadie and head for Ribagnac. La Rayre is then signposted to the left.

Appellations: Bergerac, Monbazillac

Price: Band B/C

Vineyard: 23 hectares planted mainly with white varieties Sémillon, Sauvignon and a little Muscadelle, aged 30 years on average. For the reds, over half is planted with Merlot, the rest split evenly between the Cabernets, average age 40 years.

Terroir: Some boulbène but mainly clay-limestone with a lot of limestone in places. Mainly south-facing which is less good for the formation of noble rot but this did not stop Vincent winning the Winemaker of the Year award in 2005 for his 2003 Monbazillac.

Viticulture: Vincent subscribes to the "lutte raisonnée" approach with little or no use of weedkillers. Plantings are at 3000 to the hectare with more recent plantings as high as 8000. Every other row is ploughed or grassed down and any fertiliser used is organic. Leaf thinning is done both mechanically and by hand and yields average 40 hl/ha. Maturity of the grapes is always gauged by tasting.

Vinification: A pneumatic press is used and after being cold settled, white wines are fermented at a low temperature in stainless steel or cement vats. Micro-oxygenation techniques are sometimes used with the reds and ageing is partly in oak barriques. La Rayre is Qualenvi certificated which guarantees traceability, amongst other things.

Visits: Every day by arrangement. French and English spoken.

History: Vincent hails from Champagne but came to Bergerac in 1993 when he worked at Château Belingard before purchasing La Rayre in 1999. Winemaker of the Year in 2005, Vincent is a qualified oenologist and his wines have won numerous awards and are particularly popular in Holland and Belgium.

The Wines: Top range is called "Les Premiers Vins"
Bergerac Sec, Bergerac Rouge, Monbazillac

Comments: We tasted the Bergerac Premier Vin 2003 which still had a bright garnet colour and a complex nose of smoke, mint and coffee, followed by spicy dark fruit flavours, well-structured with a medium finish. The award-winning Monbazillac 2003 was amber in colour with intense raisined fruit, honey and figs, the emphasis on fruit rather than sweetness.

In the U.K.: Not available.

Château Tour des Gendres

Owner: De Conti family
Winemaker: Luc de Conti
Address: 24240 Ribagnac
Tel: (0)5 53 57 12 43
Fax: (0)5 53 58 89 49
Email: familledeconti@wanadoo.fr
How to get there: From Bergerac take the N21 Agen road and after 12 km. at Bouniagues turn right towards Ribagnac and follow the signs for "Tour des Gendres".
Appellations: Bergerac, Côtes de Bergerac
Price: Band B/C
Vineyard: 50 hectares in the communes of Saint Julien d'Eymet, Sadillac and Ribagnac, planted with Merlot (40%), Cabernet Sauvignon (30%) and Malbec (30%), and for the whites, Sémillon (50%), Sauvignon (30%) and Muscadelle (20%). The vines are about 30 years old.
Terroir: The three different sites bring their own terroir: at "Les Gendres", clay-limestone soils with Monbazillac marl; at "Les Grands Cailloux", clay-limestone with Castillon marl; and at Saint Julien d'Eymet, clay-limestone and clay silt with Agenais marl.
Viticulture: Tour des Gendres is certified organic and is planted at up to 6500 vines to the hectare, with yields from 25 to 50 hl/ha depending on the terroir and the planting density. The vines are pruned on the single Guyot system with only 5 or 6 bunches per vine. The soil is hoed between vines and between rows it is either grassed down or planted with barley. Only composts produced on the farm are used when necessary. Luc also uses some biodynamic decoctions against pests.
Vinification: The whites are macerated on the skins for 48 hours, cold settled without any addition of enzymes and fermented either in stainless steel or in Allier oak for the Moulin des Dames. They remain on the fine lees for up to a year with little or no filtration before bottling. The reds undergo a long fermentation with some use of micro-oxygenation and are matured in oak barriques of which half are new. They are neither fined nor filtered.
Visits: Monday to Saturday, from 9.00 a.m. to 12.00 a.m. and 2.00 p.m. to 6.00 p.m. French and English spoken.
History: In the 12th century, the property was the wine farm of the Château de Bridoire, and was built on the site of a gallo-roman villa. Luc and Martine de Conti bought the property in 1981, Jean and Carole de Conti buying Grands Cailloux the same year. The brothers brought the vineyard back to life and sold their first bottles in 1987. Three years later they were joined by cousin Francis and his 20 hectares in Saint Julien d'Eymet. Luc has spearheaded quality wine production in Bergerac and is a leading exponent of organic viticulture though he has never used it as a sales tool.
The Wines: Moulin des Dames Bergerac Sec and Côtes de Bergerac Rouge
            La Gloire de Mon Père
            Cuvée des Conti
Comments: Interesting contrast between the Cuvée des Conti with its pronounced nose of citrus and tropical fruit and refreshing acidity and the heavier oaked Moulin des Dames, with perfumed nose and tones of honey and peach. Excellent reds too with the Gloire de Mon Père showing mellow fruit and soft tannins, the Moulin des Dames, spicy dark berry fruit with well-integrated tannins and a long finish.
In the U.K.: Les Caves de Pyrène, tel: 01483-538820

Monbazillac (West)

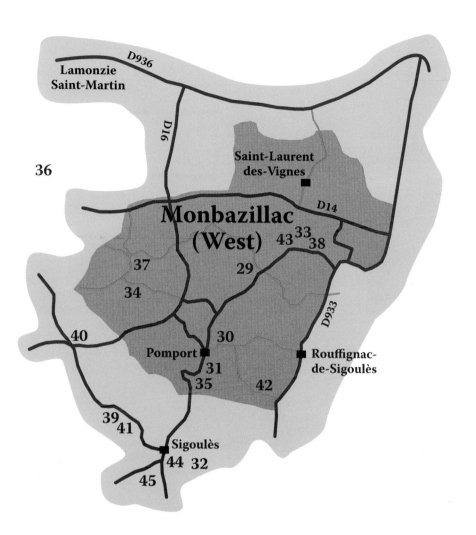

D936

Lamonzie
Saint-Martin

D16

36

Saint-Laurent
des-Vignes

D14

**Monbazillac
(West)**

43 33 38

37

29

34

D933

40

30

Pomport

Rouffignac-
de-Sigoulès

31

35

42

39 41

Sigoulès

44 32

45

29.
*Château
Belingard*

30.
*Domaine de la
Borie Blanche*

31.
*Domaine
du Boyer*

32.
*Château
Cluzeau*

33.
Château
le Fagé

34.
Domaine de
Grange Neuve

35.
Château les
Hauts de Caillevel

36.
Château
Haut Lamouthe

37.
Domaine du
Haut Montlong

38.
Château
Ladesvignes

39.
Château
le Mayne

40.
Domaine de
Moulin Pouzy

41.
Domaine
Prouillac

42.
Château
la Robertie

43.
Château
de Sanxet

44.
Cave de Sigoulès

45.
Clos des
Terrasses

Château Belingard

Owner: GFA de Belingard et Chayne
Winemaker: Comte Laurent de Bosredon
Address: 24240 Pomport
Tel: (0)5 53 58 28 03
Fax: (0)5 53 58 38 39
Email: contact@belingard.com
How to get there: From Bergerac take the D933 Mont-de-Marsan road. After 7 km. turn right on the D17 at the Grappe d'Or restaurant. After 2.2 km. take a small road on the right and the entrance is 150m on the left.
Appellations: Bergerac, Côtes de Bergerac, Monbazillac
Price: Band B
Vineyard: A large holding of 85 hectares, planted with Merlot, Cabernet Sauvignon, Cabernet Franc and Malbec, and for the whites, Sémillon, Sauvignon and Muscadelle. The vines are 25 to 30 years old. Vines are split between sites at Pomport and Monestier.
Terroir: Clay-limestone on Agenais molasse, a sedimentary formation of sand and silt.
Viticulture: A "lutte raisonnée" approach is adopted regarding the health of the vineyard and organic fertilisers are used. The soils are ploughed and grassing down is practised between rows. The vineyard is being planted at a density of up to 6000 vines per hectare.
Vinification: Grapes are harvested by machine and by hand for certain cuvées. Pneumatic and horizontal presses are used and fermentation takes place in stainless steel. The whites undergo a cold maceration prior to fermentation and are matured on the lees. The reds are de-stemmed and after cool maceration, the cuvaison lasts up to 24 days. The malolactic takes place in either tank or barrique. French oak is used to mature the top cuvées and the Monbazillac.
Visits: Monday to Friday from 9.00 a.m. to 7.00 p.m. Saturdays during the season from 10.00 a.m. to 6.00 p.m. By appointment out of season.
History: The name Belingard is of Celtic origin, from Belen-Gaard, garden of the Sun God. Winemaking here goes back to the time of the Druids and a sculpted rock harks back to a time of sacrificial altars some 3000 years ago. The vineyards were planted by monks in the eighth century and the place is steeped in history, the Hundred Years War having started just 500 metres away at Montcuq. Laurent de Bosredon took over the family estate in 1980 leaving his career in Paris in international marketing. He has worked with renowned oenologists Denis Dubourdieux, Yves Glories and more recently Pierre Guérin, and has always been ready to embrace new technology.
The Wines: Blanche de Bosredon Monbazillac
Ortus de Château Belingard Côtes de Bergerac Rouge
Comments: Multi-award winners in Blaye, Paris and Macon, and in Decanter WTC and the International Wine Challenge. The Ortus was outstanding with a complex nose of tobacco, tar and mint, a depth of ripe black fruits, soft and mellow, smoke and toast from new oak maturation and the softest of tannins.

In the U.K.: Hayman, Barwell & Jones Ltd., tel: 020 7922 1611

Domaine de la Borie Blanche

Owner/Winemaker: Emmanuelle
& Jean-Luc Ojeda

Address: 24240 Pomport

Tel: (0)5 53 73 02 45

Fax: (0)5 53 73 02 45

How to get there: As you enter the village
of Pomport from Bergerac, take the C202 on
the left towards Rouffignac and the domain
is 400m on the left.

Appellations: Bergerac, Monbazillac

Price: Band B

Vineyard: Just 3 hectares planted with Sémillon (70%), Muscadelle (20%) and Sauvignon (10%) and for the reds, half and half Merlot and Cabernet Sauvignon. The white grapes for the Monbazillac are 55 years old on average.

Terroir: Clay-limestone soils.

Viticulture: Jean-Luc has a "lutte raisonnée" approach and the vineyard is totally grassed down. Leaf thinning takes place when necessary and green harvesting is systematic. Vines are planted at 3000 to the hectare with new plantings at up to 5000.

Vinification: Inert gases are used to prevent oxidation and fermentation is temperature-controlled in stainless steel or French oak barriques which are new or one year old. The Bergerac Rouge and Monbazillac spend 12 to 13 months in oak.

Visits: Monday to Saturday, 9.00 a.m. to 12.00 a.m. and 2.00 p.m. to 7.00 p.m. French, English, Spanish and German spoken.

History: After a career in tourism, Jean-Luc acquired the property in 1995. His micro-cuvées are all sold direct to private customers. A gîte and chambre d'hôte are available on site. Jean-Luc is also keen to promote his Swin Golf course which is adjacent. This is an ingenious adaptation of the game of golf which is played with one club and a larger softer version of a standard golf ball.

The Wines: Monbazillac

Comments: The Monbazillac was a very sweet example with a rich citrussy nose and a fat oily texture filled with honeyed orange peel and had good weight in the mouth that made it a likely partner for chocolate and blue cheese.

In the U.K.: Not available.

Domaine du Boyer

Owner/Winemaker: Yannick Dumonteil

Address: Le Boyer, 24240 Pomport

Tel: (0)5 53 58 64 37

Fax: (0)5 53 58 84 47

Email: yannick.dumonteil008@orange.fr

How to get there: Take the D933 from Bergerac, then turn right on the D17 to Pomport and once in the village, turn left by the church and follow the signs to the property.

Appellations: Bergerac, Monbazillac

Price: Band A/B

Vineyard: 15 hectares, two-thirds planted with white varieties; Sémillon (75%) and Sauvignon (25%). The remainder is planted with Merlot (60%), Cabernet Sauvignon (20%), Cabernet Franc (15%) and Malbec (5%). The vines are 30 to 40 years old.

Terroir: The majority is on a clay-limestone plateau on a rocky base. Two other parcels are of limestone and boulbène soils.

Viticulture: A "lutte raisonnée" approach with 70% of the vineyard now planted at 5000 vines to the hectare. Some parcels are grassed down and others ploughed every other row, alternating every two years. Leaf thinning is done by hand, in mid-July for the reds. Green harvesting is not always needed but is done when necessary.

Vinification: The white wines are macerated on the skins and cold settled in cement vats before being fermented in stainless steel. The press is pneumatic and the Monbazillac and top red wines are matured in oak, one third of which is new.

Visits: Every day, 9.00 a.m. to 6.00 p.m. Best to ring beforehand, out of season. French, English, Italian and Vietnamese spoken.

History: The estate has been in the family since 1936. Yannick took over the reins in 1995 with his wife Ghislaine and is a third generation winemaker. He has increased the size of the holding from 9 hectares and has modernised the winery. There is a gîte and chambre d'hôte on site.

The Wines: Bergerac Le Rougier
Monbazillac

Comments: The oak-aged Le Rougier was great value with its aromas of damsons, spice and vanilla and a palate of rich dark fruits enhanced by the oak and complemented by soft tannins. The Monbazillac was of medium weight, with an orange blossom nose, honeyed orange fruit and a touch of acidity on the finish.

In the U.K.: Not available.

Château Cluzeau

Owner/Winemaker: Saury family

Address: 24240 Flaugeac

Tel: (0)5 55 24 33 71

Fax: (0)5 55 24 33 71

Email: chateau.cluzeau@yahoo.fr

How to get there: Once you get to Sigoulès, it is close to the "lycée agricole".

Appellations: Bergerac, Côtes de Bergerac, Monbazillac

Price: Band B

Vineyard: 11 hectares planted with Sémillon (70%), Sauvignon (15%) and Muscadelle (15%) and for the reds, Merlot (70%) and Cabernet Sauvignon (30%). The vines are 30 to 40 years old.

Terroir: Silty alluvial soil with limestone and clay-limestone soils on slopes facing south-south-west.

Viticulture: The Saury family is moving towards organic production with certification due in 2009 and also uses some bio-dynamic principles. 5000 vines are planted to the hectare and every other row is grassed down with hoeing beneath the vines to prevent compaction of the soil. No chemical weed-killers are used. Leaf thinning is carried out by hand, as is the harvest with yields kept to 35 to 40 hl/ha..

Vinification: Small stainless steel tanks are used for temperature-controlled fermentation, the whites having undergone a cool maceration on the skins. Pigeage is done pneumatically for the reds and micro-oxygenation techniques are used. Oak barriques are used to mature some cuvées for up to 16 months, 40% new, the rest one year old. The barrels come from the family's own cooperage business which has been in existence since 1920.

Visits: Monday to Friday, by arrangement. French and English spoken.

History: The Saury family took over the property in 2003 producing their first vintage in 2005. Awards have quickly followed, the Monbazillac being selected in Paris as being in the top twenty of the appellation.

The Wines: Côtes de Bergerac Cuvée Empyrée
Bergerac Sec Cuvée Envol
Bergerac Sec Château Cluzeau
Monbazillac

Comments: The Bergerac Sec Château Cluzeau had a nose of buttered toast and honey, with soft apricot and peach fruit, a buttery mouthfeel and just a hint of acidity on the finish. L'Envol was heavier and more complex, pineapple and tropical fruit flavours with hints of honey, liquorice and coconut. The reds tasted were excellent, the pick being the L'Empyrée which was deep and dense in colour, oaky vanillas and blackcurrants on the nose and a palate of rich black fruits, warm and mellow, well-integrated tannins and a long finish. The Monbazillac Bois Blanc had a clean honey and orange blossom nose with sweet pineapple fruit flavours and a hint of lime marmalade, sweet but not cloying.

In the U.K.: Not available.

Château le Fagé

Owner/Winemaker: Gérardin family

Address: 24240 Pomport

Tel: (0)5 53 58 32 55

Fax: (0)5 53 24 57 19

Email: info@chateau-le-fage.com

How to get there: Leave Bergerac on the D933, the Marmande road and after about 8 km., at the top of the hill at the restaurant La Grappe d'Or, turn right. After 900m. turn right again towards Château de Sanxet and after another 900m. the property is on the right.

Appellations: Bergerac Rouge, Sec, Rosé; Côtes de Bergerac Moelleux; Monbazillac

Price: Band B

Vineyard: 39 ha. on the favoured northern slopes of Monbazillac, planted with Merlot and Cabernet Sauvignon, Sauvignon, Sémillon and Muscadelle. Vines average 20-25 years of age but those used for the Monbazillac are up to 60 years old.

Terroir: Clay-limestone soils with some siliceous clay and boulbène.

Viticulture: A traditional approach with grassing down between rows, except for younger vines, and a "lutte raisonnée" policy towards spraying, depending very much on climatic conditions. Leaf thinning is effected by machine in early July on the eastern side and on the western side in August by burning the lower leaves. Grapes for dry whites and reds are harvested by machine but are prepared beforehand.

Vinification: The Bergerac appellation wines are vinified in tank whilst the prestige cuvées are vinified in oak. In a break with tradition, François produces a Bergerac Rouge entirely from Merlot and a Bergerac Sec which is 100% Sauvignon. Fermentations are generally slow and cool and micro-oxygenation is used on occasions when necessary.

Visits: Monday to Friday, 9.00 a.m. to 12.30 p.m. and 1.30 p.m. to 6.30 p.m. Weekends by arrangement. French, English and Spanish are spoken.

History: The property has been in the Gérardin family for 250 years and enjoys a spectacular view over the Dordogne valley. François, Benoît and Brigitte are the current owners keeping up the family tradition. They completely refurbished the winery in 2004 to produce wines with the emphasis on fruit and richness, long-lasting wines to drink straight away!

The Wines: Bergerac Rouge
Bergerac Sec Sauvignon
Monbazillac

Comments: An interesting comparison to be made here between the Bergerac Sec Sauvignon and the oaked Cuvée Maurice which exemplify the different styles that are made in the region. The Bergerac Rouge has won gold in Paris with its soft and spicy, fruit-driven style and the Monbazillac we tasted had delicious pineapple fruit and was relatively light in style with 20% non-botrytised grapes.

In the U.K.: Tanners Wines Ltd.: 01743 234500

Domaine de Grange Neuve

Owner/Winemaker: Castaing family

Address: 24240 Pomport

Tel: (0)5 53 58 42 23

Fax: (0)5 53 61 35 50

Email: fmcastaing@aol.com

How to get there: From Bergerac take the Marmande road and after 5 km, at the top of the hill, follow the sign to Pomport on the right, also signed Base de loisirs. Continue on the D17 for 4 km till you arrive in a small wood and a junction with a road on the right to Cunèges, Lamonzie St Martin and Grange Neuve. In 800m at the crossroads go straight across and the domain is 500m on the right.

Appellations: Bergerac Rouge, Sec, Rosé; Côtes de Bergerac Moelleux; Monbazillac

Price: Band A

Vineyard: About 60 hectares, more than half planted with Sémillon (80%), Sauvignon (10%) and Muscadelle (10%) and for the reds Merlot (60%), Cabernet Franc (20%) and Cabernet Sauvignon (20%). The vines are 25 years old and roughly one hectare is renewed each year to keep a balance between young and old vines.

Terroir: Clay, siliceous and limestone soils on slopes that are between 50 and 180 metres above sea level.

Viticulture: The vines are planted at a density of 3300 to the hectare, pruned to the Single Guyot system with 7 to 9 buds retained. Leaf thinning is done mechanically on the eastern side with alternate rows being ploughed or grassed down. Harvesting is both by machine and by hand depending on the wine.

Vinification: All the wines are vinified in temperature-controlled stainless steel vats. The whites are cold settled and selected yeasts are used which bring out the aromatic qualities of the wines. The dry white macerates overnight before fermentation and spends a short time on the fine lees. The reds are matured for a year in tank or barrel depending on the cuvée.

Visits: Monday to Friday, 9.00 a.m. to 12.00 a.m. and 1.30 p.m. to 6.30 p.m. Weekends by arrangement. French and a little English spoken.

History: The history of the property is linked to the Pichon and Castaing families who have gradually increased the vineyard holding from a mere 4 hectares in 1898 to its present 60 hectares. Three generations of the Castaing family currently work at Grange Neuve, their doctrine being to produce quality wines which represent value for money.

The Wines: Monbazillac

Comments: The Monbazillac stood out: bright golden colour with aromas of honey, freshly cut hay and a whiff of Old Holborn tobacco! Flavours of sweet citrus fruits, orange peel, with a rich, oily texture and a long, long finish.

In the U.K.: Boutinot Ltd., tel: 0161 908 1300

Château les Hauts de Caillevel

Owner/Winemaker: Sylvie Chevallier
Address: 24240 Pomport
Tel: (0)5 53 73 92 72 **Fax:** (0)5 53 73 92 72
Email: caillevel@wanadoo.fr
How to get there: In the village of Pomport as you
leave on the Sigoulès road.
Appellations: Bergerac Rouge, Sec, Rosé; Côtes
de Bergerac; Monbazillac
Price: Band B
Vineyard: 20 hectare property with slightly more red
than white varieties. In addition to the statutory Sémillon, Sauvignon and Muscadelle, there
is also a little Sauvignon Gris and Chenin for the whites, Merlot, Cabernet Franc and Cabernet
Sauvignon for the reds. Some of the vines are 80 years old.
Terroir: The property is situated on the edge of the plateau and enjoys two distinct terroirs.
On the plateau, soils are clay with iron deposits on limestone which gives a minerality to the
old vine Sémillon and Muscadelle. On the south-facing slopes which descend to the
Gardonnette, the poor stony soils of clay, sand and silt over Agenais molasse are well-suited
to the red grape varieties.
Viticulture: The domain supports the "lutte raisonnée" approach and is converting to organic
farming. Natural composts based on horse manure are used, and there is a policy of minimal
intervention in the vineyard, and indeed in the chai.
Vinification: Most of the fermentation takes place in stainless steel though some of the
smaller cuvées such as "Le Rosé des Bois", the Bergerac Sec "L'Atypique" and the
Monbazillac "Muscad'elle" and "Grains de Folie" are vinified in oak barriques. By and large,
the reds are unfined and unfiltered. Use of sulphur is kept to a minimum. Sylvie and Marc
produce a range of micro-cuvées out of a desire to try new ideas as relative newcomers to
the profession.
Visits: By arrangement, every day except Sundays, from 9 a.m. to 12 a.m. and 2 p.m. to 6
p.m. French and English spoken.
History: Sylvie Chevallier and her partner Marc Ducrocq took over the 18th century Château in
1999 having till then worked as events organisers in Paris, involved for example in the Tour de
France and the Paris-Dakar rally. It was Marc who first had the idea of their becoming
winemakers and they both retrained in Beaune. The watchwords here are fruit, structure and
minerality. Their efforts have been rewarded with a string of awards and in the Concours des
Jeunes Talents du Vin, a competition for those under 45 years of age and with less than 15 years
in the business, they were elected "Raisins d'Or" for their 2003 Monbazillac Grains de Folie.
The Wines:　　　　Monbazillac Grains de Folie / Côtes de Bergerac Terres Chaudes
　　　　　　　　　　Côtes de Bergerac Ebène / Bergerac Sec L'Atypique
Comments: The "Terres Chaudes" Côtes de Bergerac is deep red in colour with smoke and
leather on the nose and a palate of rich damson and blackberry fruit with well-integrated oak
and soft tannins on the finish. Even more concentrated, with a nose of smoke, toast and tar,
the "Ebène" is big and chewy with intense spicy black fruit flavours, softening tannins but not
over-extracted. These are not easy-drinking wines but are a tribute to the skill and adventure
of winemakers Marc and Sylvie, a charming couple who will afford you a warm welcome.
In the U.K: Imperial Wine Co. tel: 01986-892911

Château Haut Lamouthe

Owner: GAEC de la Mouthe

Winemaker: Durand brothers

Address: 56 Route de Lamouthe, 24680 Lamonzie St Martin

Tel: (0)5 53 24 07 73

Fax: (0)5 53 74 33 13

Email: chateauhautlamouthe@wanadoo.fr

How to get there: Take the D933 Marmande road out of Bergerac, then turn right on the D14 after the Monbazillac Co-operative, take the sixth road on the right towards Lamouthe and after 300m take the first track on the left.

Appellations: Bergerac Rouge, Rosé

Price: Band A

Vineyard: Ten hectares devoted to the production of red and rosé wines, planted with Merlot, Cabernet Franc and Cabernet Sauvignon, on the left bank of the Dordogne.

Terroir: On the edge of the Monbazillac appellation, soils are gravels and clays which drain well but have good reserves of water.

Viticulture: "Lutte raisonnée" approach with methods that respect the environment. Older plantings are at 3300 vines per hectare, with new vines going in at 4000 to the hectare. Organic fertilisers are used when necessary after soil analysis. Leaf and bunch thinning take place as required and the vines are trimmed by machine (rognage) four times a year. Harvesting is by machine and yields are at 50 hl/ha.

Vinification: Grapes are de-stemmed and pass through a pneumatic press to stainless steel tanks where they undergo a long cuvaison. The rosé is produced by the saignée method and is cool fermented.

Visits: By appointment. French and a little English spoken.

History: In 1986 Christian and Michel Durand decided to concentrate on viticulture and after replanting and acquiring further parcels, they were eventually joined by their third brother Alain in 1997. Two years later, they invested in new equipment and renovated the chai. In 2001 they made a conscious decision to adopt methods that are environmentally friendly.

The Wines: Bergerac Rouge
Bergerac Rosé

Comments: The Rosé had a heavily perfumed nose, strawberries with a hint of boiled sweets and bubble gum, the palate was crisp and clean with soft strawberry and rosehip fruit. The Bergerac Rouge had red fruits on the nose with a hint of leather and smoke, then spicy red fruits in the mouth, dryish and medium bodied, still with tannins to the fore.

In the U.K.: Not available.

Domaine du Haut Montlong

Owner/Winemaker: Sergenton family
Address: 24240 Pomport
Tel: (0)5 53 58 81 60
Email: sergenton-haut-montlong@wanadoo.fr
How to get there: Take the Bordeaux road from Bergerac and after about 5 km at Lamonzie St Martin turn left on the road to Le Monteil. Go through the village and continue on the D16, crossing the D14, and look out for a sign on your right.
Appellations: Bergerac, Côtes de Bergerac, Monbazillac
Price: Band B
Vineyard: 48 hectares planted with Merlot, Cabernet Sauvignon and Franc for the reds, Sémillon, Muscadelle and Sauvignon for the whites. Vines are 20 years old on average.
Terroir: Gravels on the plain for the reds, limestone on south-facing slopes also for the reds and clay-limestone on north-facing slopes for the whites.
Viticulture: The Sergenton family adopts a "lutte raisonnée" approach in the vineyard. Planting density is 4500 to 5000 vines to the hectare with alternate rows grassed down or ploughed. Leaf thinning is practised on both sides for reds and whites and green harvesting for the best cuvées. Yields average 20 hl/ha for the Monbazillac and 40 to 50 for the reds.
Vinification: The dry white is macerated on the skins for up to 24 hours, the juice gently extracted by pneumatic press and fermented at 18 degrees with four months on the lees. The red grapes are carefully sorted, de-stemmed and fermented at 30 to 32 degrees. Maceration times and the amount of pumping over will depend on analysis and tasting during fermentation. There is some use of new oak for the top cuvées, including the Monbazillac "Font Romaine".
Visits: Monday to Friday, 9.00 a.m. to 12.00 a.m. and 2.00 p.m. to 7.00 p.m. Weekend by appointment. French, English and Spanish spoken.
History: René Sergenton bought the property in 1950 when there were only 6 hectares. He handed over to his son Alain in 1980 and the property has continued to grow with new parcels and different terroirs being added over the years. Alain and Josy's daughters, along with their husbands, have joined their parents and perpetuated a family tradition that goes back to the 17th century. Chambres d'hôte are available at the domain as well as a gîte with swimming pool.
The Wines: Côtes de Bergerac Rouge Les Vents d'Anges
                  Monbazillac Font Romaine
Comments: The Les Vents d'Anges had a fragrant floral nose with hints of tobacco and in the mouth, fruits of the forest with discreet vanillas from a year in new oak, a touch of spice and liquorice and a dry, tangy finish. The Monbazillac Font Romaine, from old-vine Sémillon, was redolent of honey and beeswax with flavours of caramelized pears, clean tasting with a long finish.

In the U.K.: Not available.

Château Ladesvignes

Owner/Winemaker: Michel Monbouché
Address: 24240 Pomport
Tel: (0)5 53 58 30 67 **Fax:** (0)5 53 58 22 64
Email: chateau.ladesvignes@wanadoo.fr
How to get there: From Bergerac take the
Marmande road and after about 5 km., at the
top of the hill, turn right on the D17 towards
Pomport. The property is 800m. on the right.
Appellations: Bergerac Rouge, Sec, Rosé;
Côtes de Bergerac Rouge, Moelleux;
Monbazillac
Price: Band A/B
Vineyard: 62 ha., 23 planted for red and 39 for white. The vines are up to 30 years old for the whites, slightly younger for the reds. The total planting is as follows: Sémillon 48%, Merlot 29%, Sauvignon 10%, Cabernet Sauvignon 4%, Cabernet Franc 4%, Muscadelle 4%, Malbec 1%. The vineyard offers fine views over Bergerac and the Dordogne valley.
Terroir: Alluvial clay and clay-limestone soils on limestone base.
Viticulture: Traditional methods but following the "lutte raisonnée" principles with a respect for the environment, one priority being the treatment of the vineyard's waste water. New plantings are at 5000 vines to the hectare and the rows are grassed down. Leaf thinning takes place on one side for the reds and both sides for the sweet whites. Green harvesting takes place twice in the season.
Vinification: The winery has been completely renovated. Dry whites have a 24-hour maceration and fermentation is temperature-controlled. Pigeage is done by hand for the Côtes de Bergerac. French oak barriques are used to mature the Pétrocore Rouge and the Monbazillac.
Visits: Open every day during the week from 9.00 a.m. to 12.00 a.m. and 1.30 p.m. to 6.00 p.m. and by appointment at weekends. Food and wine tastings every Thursday in July and August. French and English spoken.
History: The Château was already mentioned in Féret's "Bergerac et ses Vins" of 1903 under the name of "A la Des Vignes". For a long time it belonged to the Marquis de Foucault and was originally a farm belonging to the Château de Bridoire. It was purchased by Michel Monbouché in 1989. Michel comes from a long line of winemakers and his great-grandfather already sold part of his production in bottle. Today, total average production amounts to 2500 hectolitres of which 35% is exported.
The Wines: Côtes de Bergerac "Velours Rouge" / Monbazillac "Automne"
                Le Pétrocore Rouge
The Pétrocore range is named after the "Petrocorii", the tribe which inhabited the Périgord in Roman times.
Comments: The Côtes de Bergerac "Velours Rouge" had a complex nose of black fruits, coffee and spice with soft and rounded fruit flavours, well-integrated tannins and dryish finish. The Pétrocore Rouge had tobacco and tar aromas, smoke and vanilla from a year in oak, still plenty of fruit on this 2002 vintage balanced by good acidity and tannins that have melted away. Good as these were, the star was the Monbazillac Automne with honeyed lemons on the nose and opulent pineapple and butterscotch flavours with a touch of requisite acidity and a long finish.
In the U.K.: Barton Brownsdon and Sadler: 020 7091 9900

Château le Mayne

Owner/Winemaker: Martrenchard family

Address: Le Mayne, 24240 Sigoulès

Tel: (0)5 53 58 40 01

Fax: (0)5 53 24 67 76

Email: vignobles-du-mayne@wanadoo.fr

How to get there: From Sigoulès, make for Gardonne and follow the signs for the property as you leave the village.

Appellations: Bergerac Rouge, Sec, Rosé; Côtes de Bergerac Rouge, Moelleux; Monbazillac

Price: Band A/B

Vineyard: 70 hectares in total in the communes of Sigoulès and Thénac and a few hectares in Monbazillac. The vineyard is south-east facing and planted with Merlot, Cabernet Sauvignon and Cabernet Franc for the reds, Sémillon, Sauvignon and Muscadelle for the whites. The vines are about 25 years old on average.

Terroir: Clay-limestone soils.

Viticulture: The vines are planted at 3300 per hectare and every other row is grassed down. Only organic fertilizers are used when necessary and yields are 55 hl/ha. Harvesting is by machine except for the Monbazillac.

Vinification: Grapes are completely de-stemmed and pass through a pneumatic press. The dry whites are macerated on the skins prior to fermentation which is temperature-controlled, for all the wines, in epoxy-lined steel and concrete vats. The Reserve wines spend some time in oak.

Visits: Monday to Friday and Saturdays during the summer, 8.00 a.m. to 12.00 a.m. and 2.00 p.m. to 6.00 p.m. Other Saturdays by arrangement. French and English spoken.

History: Château Le Mayne belonged to the Martrenchard family as far back as the 1800s. It appeared in the Féret guide of 1903 when it was the property of a Monsieur Vallade, the maternal great-grandfather of Jean-Pierre Martrenchard. The estate has been added to over the years with seven hectares in Monbazillac being acquired in 1980. The development has seen a huge investment in the winery, always in the Périgourdin style of architecture.

The Wines: Bergerac Sec
   Bergerac Rosé

Comments: The Bergerac Sec is pale lemon in colour with a floral and fruity nose and on the palate fresh clean citrus fruit, a touch of grapefruit and a soft almost honeyed finish. The Rosé is almost "clairet" in colour and shot through with strawberry fruit both on the nose and palate which is balanced by refreshing acidity and a soft and persistent finish.

In the U.K.: Not available as yet but they are part of a group of four producers looking to commercialise their "Dordogne Shire" range in the U.K. supermarket sector.

Domaine de Moulin Pouzy

Owner/Winemaker: Castaing family
Address: La Font du Roc, 24240 Cunèges
Tel: (0)5 53 58 41 20
Fax: (0)5 53 58 02 29
Email: info@moulin-pouzy.com
How to get there: From the D936, turn off at Gardonne towards Cunèges/Sigoulès on the D15. As you enter Cunèges, the domain is on the left.
Appellations: Bergerac Rouge, Sec, Rosé; Côtes de Bergerac; Monbazillac
Price: Band A

Vineyard: Planting on this 40 hectare site is mainly Merlot (95%) with some Cabernet Sauvignon and Cabernet Franc for the reds, and Sémillon (85%) with 10% Sauvignon and 5% Muscadelle. Vines are 30 to 35 years old at a density of 4000 to the hectare.

Terroir: In the commune of Cunèges, the soils are heavy clay and limestone on a Castillon limestone base and clay-limestone at the bottom of the slope. In Pomport, similar soils on the slopes with hydromorphic gravels on the lower ground.

Viticulture: The vines are trained on a single Guyot system with 6 to 9 buds, depending on each vine. Spaces between rows are grassed down, shoots are removed by hand and there is a "lutte raisonnée" approach to spraying against pests and diseases. Harvesting is by hand and by machine, with careful sorting at the chai. Yields are from 27 hl/ha for the Monbazillac to 55 hl/ha.

Vinification: Epoxy-lined concrete, glass fibre and stainless steel tanks are used, temperature being controlled both before and during fermentation. The Monbazillac Prestige is fermented in barrique and both Prestige cuvées are matured in French and American oak.

Visits: Monday to Friday, 8.30 a.m. to 12.00 a.m. and 2.00 p.m. to 6.30 p.m. French and English spoken.

History: The Domaine has been in the Castaing family since its creation on 1898. Five generations of winemakers have gradually increased the size of the vineyard over the years and in the nineties a new winery was built to house the modern equipment and tanks, along with a new tasting room. A barrel store was added in 2005 for the maturation of the Prestige cuvées.

The Wines: A wide range to choose from here, including bag-in-a-box.

          Bergerac Rosé
          Bergerac Rouge Prestige
          Monbazillac
          Monbazillac Prestige

Comments: Plenty of choice but in the end we definitely preferred the Monbazillacs. The 2003 was bright yellow with rich oily texture of orange fruit and a refreshing touch of acidity. On balance, it might perhaps be worth paying a bit more for the Prestige which had greater depth of flavour, honey, toast and Seville orange marmalade with subtle use of American oak and it coped well with dark chocolate.

In the U.K.: Not available

Domaine Prouillac

Owner/Winemaker: Michel Prouillac

Address: Le Mayne, 24240 Sigoulès

Tel: (0)5 53 58 40 92

Fax: (0)5 53 61 70 94

How to get there: Take the D15 out of Sigoulès towards Cunèges and the property is on the left just after Château Le Mayne.

Appellations: Bergerac Rouge, Sec, Rosé

Price: Band A

Vineyard: 12 hectares, eight planted for reds with Merlot, Cabernet Franc and Cabernet Sauvignon, the rest with Sémillon and Sauvignon. The vines are from ten to 60 years old.

Terroir: North-facing slopes, clay limestone soils with some flint and sand.

Viticulture: Michel has a "lutte raisonnée" approach with some organic procedures too. He sprays with powdered bentonite clay after flowering to protect against rot, oidium and mildew. After pruning the vine, each cut is covered with trichoderma which is an organic predator of other mushrooms. In the Spring, every other bud is sacrificed and this obviates the need for green harvesting later in the year. Every other row is planted with clover or flowers which attract insects and provide cover for wildlife. The canopy is trimmed in early June by machine and then finished by hand. Yields are 45-50 hl/ha. Most harvesting is by hand.

Vinification: The dry white benefits from 12 hours on the skins before a slow fermentation and then nine months on the lees. There is no use of oak for any of the wines. A Côtes de Bergerac liquoreux is produced mainly from old vine Sémillon, planted in 1946.

Visits: Open all year from 9.00 a.m. to 12.00 a.m. and 2.00 p.m. to 6.00 p.m. Weekends by arrangement. French and a little English spoken.

History: The Prouillac family has been making wine for 200 years with Michel taking over in 1980. He has been a staunch supporter of the Sigoulès wine fair missing only one in over thirty years and being voted Winemaker of the Year in 2003. There is a permanent collection of paintings by one of his employees, Didier Navas, and these have been used to some effect on the wine labels.

The Wines: Bergerac Sec
Côtes de Bergerac liquoreux
Bergerac Rosé
Bergerac Rouge

Comments: Pick of the bunch here are the Côtes de Bergerac liquoreux. We tasted the 2003 and 2002. The first is deep lemon in colour with well-defined flavours of grapefruit backed by honeyed sweetness which is never cloying. The 2002 earned Michel the "Winemaker of the Year" award and it is not difficult to see why. It is deeper in colour with a sweet marmalade nose and intense tangerine fruit flavours, a touch more complexity and well-balanced.

In the U.K.: Not available.

Château la Robertie

Owner: Brigitte & Jean-Philippe Soulier
Winemaker: Brigitte Soulier
Address: 24240 Rouffignac de Sigoulès
Tel: (0)5 53 61 35 44 **Fax:** (0)5 53 58 53 07
Email: chateau.larobertie@wanadoo.fr
How to get there: From Bergerac take the
Eymet/Marmande road. Follow the D933 as far as
Rouffignac de Sigoulès. Go through the village and
after about 2 km. turn right on the C3, direction
Pomport. The Château is 500 m. on the right.
Appellations: Bergerac Rouge, Sec, Rosé; Côtes de Bergerac; Monbazillac
Price: Band B
Vineyard: About 15 hectares of vines up to 50 years old. Recent plantings are at 5500 vines
to the hectare. Varieties planted are Merlot 49%, Cabernet Sauvignon 35%, Cabernet Franc
14%, Malbec 2% and for the whites, Sémillon 80%, Sauvignon 16% and Muscadelle 4%.
Terroir: There are two distinct soil types here as the property extends over two communes,
Rouffignac and Flaugeac. The former has more clay soils and is planted with both red and
white varieties whereas Flaugeac is on a limestone plateau with higher iron levels and is used
for reds only.
Viticulture: The Souliers are committed to producing high quality fruit and high quality wine.
Their "lutte raisonnée" approach will shortly become certified bio-dynamic. De-budding in the
Spring helps to keep yields low, less than 45 hl/ha for the reds and only 20 hl/ha for the
Monbazillac. They have enlisted the help of Julien Sroka for management of the vineyard.
Vinification: The following principles are always followed. The grapes are moved by
conveyor-belt rather than being pumped to the tanks. The whites and rosé undergo
maceration on the skins whilst the reds have a cool maceration before fermentation.
Fermentation is temperature-controlled and native yeasts are used for the top cuvées. There
is some fermentation and maturation in oak barriques, 6 to 24 months in the case of the
Monbazillac. Well-known oenologists Jean-Marc Dournel and Patricia Delayre are used as
consultants.
Visits: Every day, 10.00 a.m. to 8.00 p.m. Best to ring first. French, English, Spanish and
German are spoken.
History: Brigitte and Jean-Philippe bought the property in 1999 and since then have set
about rebuilding the vineyard, the winery and the reputation of the wine itself. Their efforts
and passion have been rewarded with a number of awards and numerous recommendations
in the wine press.
The Wines: Bergerac Rosé
                 Côtes de Bergerac: Robertie Haute and E de la Robertie
                 Monbazillac and Monbazillac Vendanges de Brumaire
Comments: The Bergeracs have had their share of success, especially the Rosé, but the
flagship wines here are the Robertie Haute and the Monbazillac Vendanges de Brumaire. We
tasted the straight Monbazillac which had a tangy citrus freshness to it which offset the
honeyed marshmallow fruit and gave it great balance. The Robertie Haute had a heavily
perfumed nose with hints of smoke and cigar box, and on the palate rich, vibrant blackberry
fruit, chewy tannins and well-balanced oak.
In the U.K.: Not available.

Château de Sanxet

Owner/Winemaker: Bertrand de Passemar

Address: 24240 Pomport

Tel: (0)5 53 58 37 46

Fax: (0)5 53 58 37 46

Email: sanxet@sanxet.com

How to get there: Take the Marmande road out of Bergerac and after 6 km take a right turn at the Grappe d'Or restaurant, towards Pomport, and after 0.7 km take a right turn and then a left after a further 0.5 km.

Appellations: Monbazillac; Bergerac Rouge, Sec, Rosé

Price: Band A

Vineyard: 18 hectares equally split between red and white varieties. The vines are 40 years old, apart from the Sauvignon.

Terroir: The vineyard is south-facing and the soils are clay-limestone, very stony and well-drained.

Viticulture: Planted at a density of 3500 vines to the hectare, every other row is grassed down and the Passemar family works to "lutte raisonnée" guidelines. Leaf thinning is done by hand on the eastern side. Yields are in line with the norm for the appellations. Harvesting is by machine except of course for the Monbazillac where there are usually three separate picks.

Vinification: The Bergerac Rouge undergoes a three week fermentation and cuvaison, followed by six months in tank and a further year in barrique. The Monbazillac spends 18 months in oak.

Visits: 9.00 a.m. to 12.00 a.m. and 2.00 p.m. to 6.00 p.m. The Château also houses an impressive collection of rare cars and racing cars.

History: The history of Sanxet goes back to the eleventh century when it was on the route to Compostella and monks first planted vines here and welcomed pilgrims. The present building is a fifteenth century manor house built on the remains of an English castle that was erected in 1280. It has been in the Sanxet family since 1619 as Bertrand's wife is a Sanxet. The cellars are underground in a tunnel which linked the Château to the fortress of Montcuq.

The Wines: Bergerac Rouge
Bergerac Sec Sauvignon
Monbazillac

Comments: If there's any 2000 Bergerac Rouge Barriques left, it might be worth snapping up a few bottles especially as it represents excellent value. It was well-structured with a nose of stewed plums and had retained a good concentration of rich dark fruits with tannins that had left a soft velvety texture. The Monbazillac 2001 was quite heavy and alcoholic in style, less complex than some with an underlying citrus tang.

In the U.K.: Not available.

Cave de Sigoulès

Owner/Winemaker: Vignerons de Sigoulès
Address: Cave de Sigoulès, 24240 Sigoulès
Tel: (0)5 53 63 78 50 **Fax:** (0)5 53 61 55 10
How to get there: Follow the D933 from Bergerac towards Eymet. Turn right on the D15, direction Sigoulès. The Cave is on the left before entering the village.
Appellations: Bergerac Rouge, Sec, Rosé; Côtes de Bergerac; Saussignac
Price: Band B
Vineyard: 1200 ha. split between 230 growers. 65% of the production is red and 35% white. Originally planted at 3500 vines to the hectare, plantings now are at 8000 per hectare. Vines are 20 to 25 years old on average and comprise Sémillon and Sauvignon, Merlot, Cabernet Sauvignon and Cabernet Franc.
Terroir: Clay and limestone. The clay retains water which limits stress from drought in the summer. White limestone rocks on the surface reflect the sun and help to ripen the grapes even in cool periods. The soil is rich in organic matter which adds structure to the soil and aids ventilation. Frequent soil analysis is carried out to check levels of magnesium, potassium and phosphates.
Viticulture: Grass is planted between rows to take up water, create competition with the vines, making the vines less vigorous and reducing yields. Foliage is encouraged in the early season to help photosynthesis. Leaf plucking takes place between the end of June and August to promote ripeness, limit rot and encourage the production of phenolics (tannins, colour and flavour compounds). Spraying has been reduced to a minimum with two anti-botrytis sprays for the whites and just one for the reds.
Vinification: The Cave de Sigoulès was the first winery in the world to use a Vinimatic rotary fermenter in 1976. It avoids the need for pumping over and being a closed tank, allows for semi-carbonic fermentation.
Visits: Monday to Saturday, 9.00 a.m. to 12.30 p.m. and 2.00 p.m. to 6.30 p.m. in May to August. In the winter, 9.00 a.m. to 12.00 a.m. and 1.30 p.m. to 5.30 p.m. French, English, Spanish, Dutch and Afrikaans are spoken.
History: The Cave de Sigoulès was created in 1939 by just 11 producers and until 1960 only vinified white wines. In 1991 it joined forces with the Montravel co-operative. It has always been in the forefront of wine production in the region, imposing a strict and rigorous doctrine on its members.
The Wines: Foncaussade / Bergerac Rouge Légende / Cantus Terra
                    Saussignac Vendanges d'Autrefois
Comments: We preferred the blended Bergerac Sec to the Sauvignon. It was very pale in colour with a citrus nose and hints too of gooseberry and lychees and in the mouth refreshing acidity backed by intense fruitiness of grapefruit and lime. With its fragrant floral nose, the Foncaussade Rosé was a glassful of strawberries and cream with a hint of cinnamon spice. The Cantus Terra was heavily oaked on the nose followed by an explosion of dark fruit flavours with spice and vanilla from softening tannins. It was rather overshadowed, however, by the Légende which was deep and dense in colour with intense rich black fruit flavours, the oak well-handled and not dominant, the finish mellow and long-lasting. The Saussignac Vendanges d'Autrefois was a rich medley of raisins, dates, figs, neroli and nuts with an aftertaste of caramelised Bramleys. Don't drink this with dessert, drink it instead of dessert!
In the U.K.: Waitrose, Sunday Times Wine Club/Laithwaites, Marks and Spencer
Communication in the U.K is managed by Lindsay-May Partnership, tel: 020 7470 8890

Clos des Terrasses

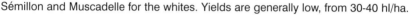

Owner/Winemaker: Catherine & Fabrice Suyrot
Address: 24240 Sigoulès
Tel: (0)5 53 63 22 60/ (0)6 60 44 80 28
Fax: (0)5 53 63 22 60
Email: fabricedesuyrot@wanadoo.fr
How to get there: Take the D933, the
Marmande/Mont-de-Marsan road out of Bergerac
until you come to the sign for Sigoulès. Follow
signs to the property.
Appellations: Bergerac Rouge, Sec, Rosé; Côtes
de Bergerac Rouge
Price: Band B
Vineyard: 14 ha on the hillsides to the south of the
Dordogne, planted with vines averaging 30 years of
age. Merlot, Cabernet Franc, Cabernet Sauvignon
and Malbec for the reds, Sauvignon Blanc and Gris,
Sémillon and Muscadelle for the whites. Yields are generally low, from 30-40 hl/ha.
Terroir: Soils are a mixture of clay and limestone.
Viticulture: The vineyard is in the process of converting to organic certification. The Suyrots
have a minimal interventionist policy, with a respect for nature and a ban on all use of
chemicals. Soils are ploughed with leaf trimming on the east side and green harvesting as
necessary.
Vinification: Grapes are carefully sorted and fermented in small thermo-regulated vats which
allow different parcels and different varieties to be vinified separately. There is minimal use of
sulphur and some malolactic takes place in selected oak barrels. The wines mature on the
lees in tank and /or oak and in general there is no fining or filtration. Thierry Bernard is the
experienced maître de chai.
Visits: May to September, 9.00 a.m. to 12.00 a.m. and 2.00 p.m. to 6.00 p.m. The rest of the
year by arrangement. French and English spoken.
History: Fabrice and Catherine, Count and Countess de Suyrot, bought the property in 2001
with the ambition of producing the best wine in Bergerac. Fabrice comes from a background
in finance and although a self-confessed devotee of Burgundy, chose this domain in the
Périgord to fulfil his dream. The reception area has been tastefully renovated.
The Wines: Le Fruit des Terrasses Rosé
                Le Fruit des Terrasses Rouge
                Le Clos des Terrasses Rouge
                Le Clos des Terrasses Blanc
                Le Clos des Terrasses Rouge Cuvée le Clos
Comments: Pick of these fine wines are the Clos des Terrasses Blanc, a blend of Sauvignon,
Sémillon and Muscadelle, vinified in barriques, matured on the lees, with a hint of honey and
smoke on the nose and pronounced citrus acidity; and the flagship Cuvée le Clos from old
vine Merlot, Cabernet Franc and Cabernet Sauvignon with up to 18 months in oak, spice and
tobacco aromas, rich cherry and damson fruit with soft velvety tannins.

In the U.K.: Wine in Cornwall Ltd., tel: 01326 379426

Saussignac

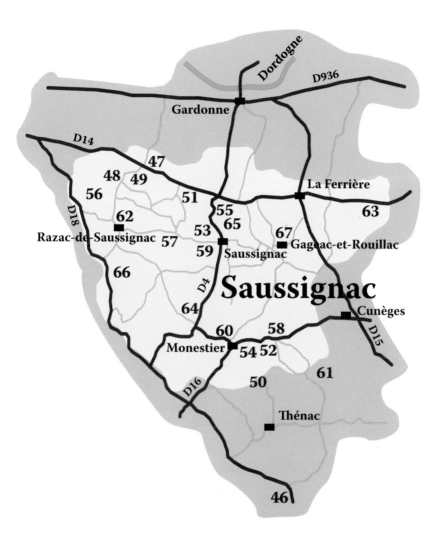

Dordogne

D936

Gardonne

D14

47

48 49

56

51

D18

62

Razac-de-Saussignac 57

55

53 65

59 Saussignac

La Ferrière

63

67

Gageac-et-Rouillac

Saussignac

D4

66

64

Cunèges

60 58

D15

Monestier 54 52

D16

50

61

Thénac

46

46.
Domaine les
Brandeaux

47.
Domaine du
Cantonnet

48.
Domaine du
Castellat

49.
Château
le Chabrier

50.
*Château
de la Colline*

51.
*Château
Court les Mûts*

52.
*Château des
Eyssards*

53.
*Château
de Fayolle*

54.
*Château
Grinou*

55.
*Château Haut
Garrigue*

56.
*Château
Lardy*

57.
*Château
La Maurigne*

58.
Clos du Mège

59.
*Château
Miaudoux*

60.
*Château
Monestier la Tour*

61.
*Château
Panisseau*

62.
*Château
le Payral*

63.
*Château
Perrou*

64.
*Château
Richard*

65.
*Château
le Tap*

66.
*Château
des Vigiers*

67.
Clos d'Yvigne

Domaine les Brandeaux

Owner/Winemaker: Jean-Marc & Thierry Piazzetta
Address: Puyguilhem, 24240 Thénac
Tel: (0)5 53 58 41 50
Fax: (0)5 53 58 41 50
Email: Thierry.piazzetta@wanadoo.fr
How to get there: From Sigoulès take the D17 towards Puyguilhem, turn left briefly on the D18 and then right on the D17 again towards Duras, looking out for "Les Brandeaux".
Appellations: Bergerac Rouge, Sec, Rosé; Côtes de Bergerac
Price: Band A

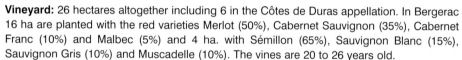

Vineyard: 26 hectares altogether including 6 in the Côtes de Duras appellation. In Bergerac 16 ha are planted with the red varieties Merlot (50%), Cabernet Sauvignon (35%), Cabernet Franc (10%) and Malbec (5%) and 4 ha. with Sémillon (65%), Sauvignon Blanc (15%), Sauvignon Gris (10%) and Muscadelle (10%). The vines are 20 to 26 years old.
Terroir: Clay-limestone slopes on the watershed of the rivers Garonne and Dordogne.
Viticulture: The Piazzetta brothers adhere to the "lutte raisonnée" approach, treating the vines in accordance with the recommendations of the A.P.V. (Agence de la Protection des Végétaux). The vines are planted at 3300 and 4500 to the hectare with every other row being ploughed or left to grass over. Compost is added when soil analysis indicates it is necessary. Foliage is thinned on the eastern side throughout the vineyard and green harvesting takes place for the liquoreux and the top reds, yields being up to 55 hl/ha. Harvesting has been by machine since 1982 except of course for the sweet wines where 3 or 4 passes are made.
Vinification: Harvesting often takes place at night and the reds have a week's cold maceration before fermentation which takes place at 24-25 degrees for the light fruity styles and 26-27 degrees for the longer-lasting cuvées. Total vatting time is up to a month and micro-oxygenation has been practised since 2007. Some of the wines spend up to a year in oak.
Visits: By arrangement. It is best to ring beforehand to make sure someone will be there.
History: The property has been put together over four generations since the first Piazzetta arrived from Italy in 1924. He bought initially at Bernac and his daughter bought a property at Puyguilhem which Jean-Louis took over in 1969. He developed and expanded the property from 5 ha. to 18 ha. by 1989 and then handed over to his sons Thierry and Jean-Marc in 2003.
The Wines: Le Nectar des Brandeaux
              Bergerac Rouge fût
              Bergerac Rouge
Comments: Of the reds, we preferred the oak-aged version. It had an earthy nose, hints of smoke and leather, and good depth of intense blackberry fruit in the mouth and softening tannins on the finish. The Nectar was not overly sweet with flavours of crystallized fruit and had an attractive aroma of jasmine, honey and vanilla ice cream with just a hint of celery and squill.
In the U.K. :Not available.

Domaine du Cantonnet

Owner/Winemaker: Jean-Paul
and Thierry Rigal

Address: Le Cantonnet, 24240
Razac-de-Saussignac

Tel: (0)5 53 27 88 63

Fax: (0)5 53 27 12 31

Email: vignobles-rigal@orange.fr

How to get there: From Gardonne,
take the road to Saussignac, turn right
on the D14 towards Razac and look
out for the sign to the property at the side of the road.

Appellations: Bergerac Sec, Rouge, Rosé; Côtes de Bergerac; Saussignac
Price: Band A/B

Vineyard: 30 hectares planted with Merlot, Cabernet Franc and Cabernet Sauvignon for the reds, Sémillon, Sauvignon Blanc and Gris for the whites. The Sémillon vines are 50 years old on average.

Terroir: Situated on the Negreaud plateau, clay-limestone and silt soils on a rocky base.

Viticulture: The oldest vines are planted at 4000 to the hectare with more recent plantings at 3000 to facilitate mechanization. Rows are grassed down completely, or every other row in some parcels, to reduce vigour. Leaf thinning is done by machine in the summer and by hand before harvest. "Lutte raisonnée" principles are followed.

Vinification: The press is pneumatic and after cold settling, fermentation is controlled at 18 to 20 degrees. The Saussignac Cuvée Cécile is fermented in barrel for 3 to 4 weeks and aged for a further year with successive rackings. The reds are de-stemmed and fermented in stainless steel or epoxy-lined cement vats. Vatting time is 8 to 12 days prior to the malolactic fermentation.

Visits: July and August, 10.00 a.m. to 6.00 p.m. Rest of the year, every day by appointment. French and English spoken.

History: Jean-Paul bought the property in 1975 and undertook a programme of replanting after the vineyard had been neglected. They raised goats too to make cheese but these were replaced by plum trees in the mid-eighties. A new winery was built in 1987 to allow for maturation in barrique. Jean-Paul was joined by his son Thierry and they formed an E.A.R.L. in 1995. Some of the production is marketed as Château Ruine de Belair. Up to 40% is exported to Belgium.

The Wines: Bergerac Sec
Bergerac Rouge Tradition

Comments: The white was based on Sauvignon Blanc with some Sauvignon Gris. It had a nettley elderflower nose with aromatic and refreshing whitecurrant and gooseberry fruit. The Bergerac Rouge was a Merlot and had a lovely cedary nose and great intensity of dark fruits, soft and velvety with no hard edges.

In the U.K.: Not available.

Domaine du Castellat

Owner/Winemaker: Jean-Luc Lescure

Address: Le Castellat, 24240 Razac-de-Saussignac

Tel: (0)5 53 27 08 83

Fax: (0)5 53 58 11 40

Email: domaine.castellat@wanadoo.fr

How to get there: From Gardonne take the road to Saussignac and at the bottom of the hill turn right on the D14 towards Razac and take the second on the left.

Appellations: Bergerac, Saussignac

Price: Band A

Vineyard: 22 hectares planted with Sémillon (50%), Muscadelle (30%) and Sauvignon (20%) and for the reds, Merlot (55%), Cabernet Sauvignon (20%), Cabernet Franc (15%) and Malbec (10%). The vines are on average 25 to 35 years old.

Terroir: For the reds, clay-limestone soils and for the whites, siliceous clays.

Viticulture: Every other row is grassed down and vines are planted at 3000 to the hectare, with new plantings at 5000. Organic fertilisers and lime are added when necessary and leaf thinning is undertaken for the reds as required. Yields are in line with the appellation and harvesting is by machine except of course for the Saussignac.

Vinification: Glass fibre and cement tanks are the norm here with some oak maturation for the top reds and the Saussignac in second-hand French barriques. Fermentation temperature is controlled at 18 degrees for the whites and rosé with maturation on the lees for the former.

Visits: Monday to Saturday, 9.00 a.m. to 12.00 a.m. and 2.00 p.m. to 5.00 p.m. French and English spoken.

History: Built on the site of fortifications as its name suggests, Castellat was a look-out post during the Hundred Years War and the Wars of Religion, commanding as it does a view over the valley of the Dordogne. Jean-Luc has been in charge here since 1983 and is a fifth generation winemaker. There is also a gîte on site.

The Wines: Bergerac Rosé
                  Saussignac
                  Bergerac Rouge Cuvée Victor et Hugo

Comments: The Bergerac Rouge was bright ruby in colour with quite a pungent earthy nose and warm black fruit flavours, hints of coffee and chocolate and a dry blackcurrant finish. The Saussignac had a pronounced honey and orange blossom nose with sweet orange marmalade fruit and good balance. Both wines offered excellent value.

In the U.K.: Not available.

Château le Chabrier

Owner/Winemaker: Pierre Carle
Address: 24240 Razac-de-Saussignac
Tel: (0)5 53 27 92 73
Fax: (0)5 53 23 39 03
Email: chateau.le.chabrier@free.fr
How to get there: On the D936 at
Gardonne, take the D4 towards Saussignac
and follow the signs to Razac-de-Saussignac
and Château le Chabrier.
Appellations: Bergerac Rouge, Sec, Rosé;
Côtes de Bergerac; Saussignac
Price: B/C

Vineyard: Overlooking the Dordogne valley, 20 hectares of vines, over 30 years old. For the reds, Merlot (45%), Cabernet Sauvignon (37%) and Cabernet Franc (18%) are planted, and for the whites, Sémillon (44%), Sauvignon (34%), Muscadelle (12%) and Ugni Blanc (10%).

Terroir: The slopes are clay-limestone and on the plateau, a thin layer of clay over a limestone base.

Viticulture: Le Chabrier has been organic for a number of years and Pierre Carle is convinced his wines taste better for it. Soils are ploughed with grassing down of alternate rows on some parcels. Only organic fertilisers are used and green harvesting is practised when necessary though short pruning generally means it is not required. Yields are very low: 20 hl/ha for dry whites and reds, a miserly 7 hl/ha for the Saussignac.

Vinification: The reds are cool macerated, fermented using indigenous yeasts, have a long cuvaison, are matured from two to four years and bottled without fining or filtration. The dry whites are macerated on the skins and matured 24 to 30 months in tank or barrique with little or no sulphur being used. The sweet whites are fermented and matured in oak for 30 to 36 months. There is no chaptalisation with any of these wines.

Visits: Every day from 10.00 a.m. to 12.00 a.m. and from 2.00 p.m. to 6.00 p.m. It is always advisable to ring first. French, English and German spoken.

History: Le Chabrier was a fortress in the Middle Ages, destroyed in 1345 at the start of the Hundred Years War by the Earl of Derby. The present Château was founded in 1640. Over the centuries, the cultivation of vines has become the principal activity and the property was bought by Pierre Carle in 1991. Pierre's grandfather bought Château Croque-Michotte in Saint Emilion in 1906 and it was Pierre's boyhood dream to become a vigneron. However, first he was to work as a railway engineer in Paris and it was only when he was married with four children that his dream was realised.

The Wines: Saussignac Cuvée Elena
          Côtes de Bergerac Cuvée Patrimoine

Comments: The Saussignac, 80% Sémillon with 15% Muscadelle and 5% Sauvignon, was stunning, with orange peel on the nose carrying through to bitter orange flavours on the palate with richness balanced by fresh acidity. Absolutely delicious. Equally impressive was the red Patrimoine. We tasted the 2001 which had retained its black cherry colour and had a complex nose of cassis, liquorice and tobacco. silky tannins and dense damson and plum fruits, again with a hint of liquorice and a pleasantly dry finish.

In the U.K.: Club Bernard, tel:01702-557514 and NH Wines Ltd., tel: 0191-2572827

Château de la Colline

Owner/Winemaker: Charles Martin
Address: 24240 Thénac
Tel: (0)5 53 61 87 87 **Fax:** (0)5 53 61 71 09
Email: charlesm@la-colline.com
How to get there: Turn off the D936 at Gardonne taking the D4 through Saussignac, past Monestier and turning left on the D18 and left again to Thénac.
Appellations: Bergerac Rouge, Sec, Rosé; Côtes de Bergerac
Price: Band B

Vineyard: 18 hectares of vines on an estate of 40 hectares, planted mainly with Merlot, with the Cabernets for the reds, and mainly with Sémillon for the whites, with Sauvignon and Muscadelle. Charles is forthright in his belief in the importance of Merlot and Sémillon in the region and feels that the fact should be exploited more when promoting the wines of the Bergeracois, even if it doesn't sit too well with the demands of the appellation.

Terroir: The vineyard is planted at the top of a hill (hence the name!), one of the highest points of the region, and is south facing, protected from the cold northerlies by a screen of trees. There are three distinct soil types: redzina with fine fragmented chalk; siliceous with quartz and flint on a clay base, good for drainage; red clay over limestone, well-suited to Merlot.

Viticulture: Charles has developed his own method of high density planting at 8000 vines to the hectare but with only 50 cm between plants and two metres between rows to allow for mechanised working. Charles was the first to use grassing down in the vineyard and is now moving towards doing so every other row. Vineyard mapping is helping to match the vines to the specific soils. Yields are 50-55 hl/ha.

Vinification: Charles is keen to try innovative approaches. He was one of the first in the region to use inert gases to protect wines from oxidation and has recently been using small swimming pools to ferment his Merlot. The cap is quite thin, the fermentation takes place much more quickly and produces wines with the emphasis on fruit. Nor is he averse to using plastic closures. He uses 500 litre barrels to age his wines which are larger than the norm and better suited to the style he wishes to achieve. Keywords here are freshness and elegance.

Visits: Visitors are welcome but it is best to ring beforehand. French and English spoken.

History: Charles Martin is a Welshman, son of a wine merchant and grandson of a formula one racing driver. He learnt his trade in Napa, Australia and New Zealand and first came to the Dordogne in 1987 as winemaker for the Rymans at Château de la Jaubertie. In 1994 he started out on his own at la Colline and quickly set about analysing the soil quality of the different parcels of land, determined to let the terroir express itself through his wines. This is reflected in the cuvées labelled "Côte Sud" which are fruity and fresh, or "Coté Ouest", more complex structured wines.

The Wines: Côté Sud red and white / Côté Ouest red and white
                   La Colline Pink / Confit de la Colline / Calista and Carminé

Comments: Dark cherry in colour, the Côté Sud red was very approachable with an intense fruity nose and rich but fresh fruit on the palate with gentle tannins. The 1999 Confit + was deep amber in colour with delicious burnt caramel flavours, liquid gold with a dash of acidity. Well wicked!

In the U.K: High Breck Vintners, tel: 020 83401848 / Imbibros, tel: 01483 861164
                Andrew Wilson Wines, tel: 01782 372888 / Fingal - Rock, tel: 01600 712372

Château Court Les Mûts

Owner/Winemaker: Pierre-Jean Sadoux
Address: 24240 Razac-de-Saussignac
Tel: (0)5 53 27 92 17
Fax: (0)5 53 23 77 21
Email: court-les-muts@wanadoo.fr
How to get there: From Gardonne take the D15 then turn right on the D14 and the property is on the left by the roadside just before Razac.
Appellations: Bergerac Rouge, Sec, Rosé; Côtes de Bergerac; Saussignac
Price: Band B

Vineyard: Sizeable vineyard of 68 hectares in the communes of Razac-de-Saussignac and Saussignac, planted half and half with white and red varieties; Sauvignon, Sémillon and Muscadelle; Merlot, Cabernet Sauvignon, Cabernet Franc and Malbec.

Terroir: Clay-limestone slopes overlooking the valley of the Dordogne.

Viticulture: Pierre-Jean adopts "lutte raisonnée" methods, overseen by the Chambre d'Agriculture, and since 2004 is affiliated to Qualenvi which also encompasses, amongst other things, care of the environment and traceability.

Vinification: The whites undergo maceration on the skins, are cold settled and fermented in tank or barrique depending on the cuvée, followed by lees stirring. The Côtes de Bergerac Rouge has a long cuvaison and spends a year in oak with light fining with egg white. The Saussignac is made from noble rot affected grapes which ferment slowly for up to 5 months in oak where they continue to mature for a further 12 to 15 months.

Visits: Monday to Friday from 9.00 a.m. to 12.00 a.m. and 2.00 p.m. to 6.00 p.m. Saturdays by arrangement. French and English spoken.

History: Pierre-Jean's father bought 14 hectares of vines in Razac in 1962 on his return from Algeria. The vines had miraculously escaped the ravages of phylloxera at the end of the nineteenth century. Pierre-Jean qualified as an oenologist and joined his parents at Court-les-Mûts in 1972. Over the next ten years the family invested heavily in the winery and new equipment. In 1987 they acquired Château Petite Borie and Château Bramefant and awards have followed thick and fast, culminating in Pierre-Jean being voted winemaker of the year for the Bergerac region in 2007.

The Wines: Côtes de Bergerac Rouge
                 Côtes de Bergerac Moelleux
                 Saussignac

Comments: Everything about the place oozes class and professionalism, and so do the wines. The red Côtes de Bergerac had good depth of colour with a spicy, cedary nose, smoke and autumn leaves, and in the mouth the 2003 had great balance with soft red fruits to the fore, the oak lightly handled making for a wine that had the finesse and elegance of an expensive claret. The Saussignac was liquid gold, a rich honeyed nose with luscious peach fruit flavours but shot through with a striking acidity that created a delightful balance.

In the U.K.: Not available.

Château des Eyssards

Owner/Winemaker: Pascal Cuisset
Address: 24240 Monestier
Tel: (0)5 53 24 36 36
Fax: (0)5 53 58 63 74
Email: eyssards@wanadoo.fr
How to get there: From Gardonne take the
D15 to Cunèges, then turn right on the D16 to
Monestier and look out for the signs to the
domain.

Appellations: Bergerac Rouge, Sec, Rosé; Saussignac
Price: Band A/B
Vineyard: Some 40 ha planted with Merlot, Cabernet Franc and Cabernet Sauvignon for the reds, and Sémillon, Sauvignon, Muscadelle and Chenin Blanc for the whites. Red varieties are 20 to 30 years old whilst the Sémillon and Muscadelle can be 45 years old.
Terroir: Clay and stony soils with chalky clays.
Viticulture: A minimum interventionist "lutte raisonnée" policy helps to maintain a healthy vineyard. Planting densities are at least 5000 vines to the hectare after significant investment in the vineyard over recent years. Apart from the hand-picked Saussignac, harvesting is done at night by machine.
Vinification: Dry whites have skin contact for 24 to 30 hours with fermentation in stainless steel tanks or in French oak of which one third is new, followed by ageing on the lees for 3 to 9 months depending on the cuvée. The reds are macerated 4 to 5 days before fermentation in stainless steel followed by a degree of oak maturation. The Prestige spends a year in oak followed by a further 5-6 months in tank before bottling. The Adagio comes from the best 45 barrels from over 250 which are tasted, and is matured in barriques of which 60% are new.
Visits: Monday to Friday, 9.00 a.m. to 12.00 a.m. and 2.00 p.m. to 6.00 p.m. French and English spoken.
History: Pascal Cuisset bought the property in 1984 and along with his father Léonce and brother Laurent created a GAEC, bringing together parcels of land at Monestier and les Billots. For the next nine years they developed the vineyard and commercialized their wines so successfully that in 1993 they were able to build a new winery and store. Pascal is bullish about the importance of making wines that give pleasure to people and of offering value for money and he certainly does both.
The Wines: Bergerac Rouge, Bergerac Sec
             Cuvées Prestige
             Saussignac
Comments: The Bergerac Sec had a grassy nose with hints of lime, the Sauvignon softened a touch by the Sémillon, creating a good balance of acidity and stone fruit. The red Bergerac from 2004 had great elegance, an earthy blackcurrant nose, with good depth of black fruit flavours, velvety tannins and a chalky dryness. The Cuvée Flavie Saussignac was a multi-dimensional cocktail of marzipan, beeswax, raisins, fruit cake and cinnamon with a definite over-ripe apple influence.

In the U.K.: PLB Wines, tel: 01342 318282

Château de Fayolle

Owner: Ringwood Brewery
Winemaker: Gilles Prugne
Address: 24240 Saussignac
Tel: (0)5 53 74 32 02 **Fax:** (0)5 53 74 51 35
Email: chateaufayolle@wanadoo.fr
How to get there: At Gardonne on the D936, between
Ste Foy la Grande and Bergerac, follow the directions to
Saussignac and then follow the signs to Château de Fayolle.
Appellations: Bergerac Rouge, Sec, Rosé; Saussignac,
Blanc de Blancs Méthode Traditionnelle
Price: Band A/B
Vineyard: 17 ha. planted with Sémillon and Sauvignon for the whites, Merlot, Cabernet Sauvignon and Cabernet Franc for the reds. The vines are 25-30 years old on average.
Terroir: Limestone-clay plateau slopes gently towards the west and is well drained. Its elevation above the Dordogne valley ensures good air flow through the vines which helps to protect against frost and disease.
Viticulture: The property follows the principles of "lutte raisonnée" and is becoming more and more organic, eschewing the use of all weed-killers. Grassing down is done either in total or in alternate rows depending on the age of the vines. There is some green harvesting with yields at 45 hl/ha and the grapes are picked by machine.
Vinification: Fermentations are temperature-controlled in stainless steel tanks after gentle pressing in a pneumatic press. Whites are macerated on the lees and there is some oak ageing, notably of the top red cuvées, the Marcassin and the Sang du Sanglier, the latter having 12 months in two-year-old oak barrels purchased from Château Haut-Brion. There is no pigeage for the reds and at 10 degrees alcohol, the wine is taken off the lees to avoid any bitterness.
Visits: Vineyard visits by arrangement, Monday to Friday. English and French spoken.
History: David Welsh was the owner of Ringwood Brewery, an independent family firm based in Hampshire. His dream was also to own a vineyard in France and after a three year search starting in 1993, he eventually fell in love with the Château de Fayolle just south of the Dordogne river. It was finally purchased from the Receiver in 1997 but only after a nightmare of frustrations. The vineyard and winery were very run down but there has been substantial investment to improve them both as well as to refurbish the Château and convert it into luxury gîte accommodation. Wine courses and "confrères" lunches are currently being organised at the Château.
The Wines: Bergerac Rouge, Sec, Rosé
                  Cuvée Marcassin
                  Cuvée Sang du Sanglier
                  Saussignac
Comments: A reminder that wild boar still roam wild in the Dordogne is seen in the two special cuvées of note, the Marcassin and the Sang du Sanglier. These are both polished wines, commercial it is true but characterful too with intense dark fruit flavours, a touch of spice and the oak well handled, slightly more evident in the "Sang du Sanglier". The Saussignac was delicious too with rich botrytised fruit and a streak of acidity. The entry-level wines produced for the British pub market are soft and fruity but more than acceptable as a house wine.
In the U.K.: Ringwood Brewery, tel: 01425 471177
                Confrères de Fayolle enquiries: 01425 484650

Château Grinou

Owner/Winemaker: Catherine & Guy Cuisset
Address: 24240 Monestier
Tel: (0)5 53 58 46 63
Fax: (0)5 53 61 05 66
Email: chateaugrinou@aol.com
How to get there: To reach the hamlet of
Monestier, turn off the D936 at Gardonne onto
the D4, heading for Saussignac and then
follow the signs to Monestier.
Appellations: Bergerac, Saussignac
Price: Band B
Vineyard: 35 hectares planted with Merlot (70%), Cabernet Franc (15%) and Cabernet Sauvignon (15%) for the reds. The vines are 35 years old. Sémillon and Sauvignon are planted for the whites, aged on average 25 years.
Terroir: Clay-limestone and siliceous clay soils on a limestone base, situated on well-drained slopes above the Dordogne.
Viticulture: Guy has a traditional approach in the vineyard and is in the process of converting to organic production. He is very conscious of health issues and looks forward to a time when organic viticulture will be the norm. He plants clover between rows which obviates the need for weed-killers, adds nitrogen and aerates the soil. The estate also treats its own waste water.
Vinification: Guy was one of the first in the area to harvest at night and also uses inert gas to retain the freshness of the grape juice and prevent oxidation. The reds have a cool maceration and commercial yeasts are used in a temperature-controlled fermentation. Micro-oxygenation is often used and the wines are aged in French and American oak. The whites are macerated on the skins and matured on the lees either in stainless steel or oak. The Saussignac and moelleux are cold-stabilised with the former spending up to 18 months in oak.
Visits: Every day but it is best to ring first to make sure someone will be there. French and English spoken and son Julien also speaks German and Danish.
History: `There has never been a Château as such here but there are remains of an earlier monastery, destroyed in the Wars of Religion, which gave the village its name. There are still the remains of a porch dating from the 12th century and evidence too in the current building that stones from the monastery have been re-used over the years. Guy inherited half his father's estate in 1978, left his job as an international lawyer and set about making a name for Château Grinou which was created in 1986. The Cuissets' motto, taken from Virgil's "Georgics" and in homage to the monks is fittingly "Labor omnia vincit improbus", meaning "Dedicated work overcomes all obstacles".
The Wines: Bergerac Sec Tradition, Grande Réserve
Bergerac Rouge Tradition, Réserve, Le Grand Vin
Saussignac
Comments: Le Grand Vin had a striking nose of some complexity - spice, vanilla, figs - followed by rich spicy fruit on the palate and good balance. The Réserve was good too with its deep ruby colour, smooth mellow fruit and dry finish. The Bergerac Sec Tradition showed a pleasing balance of soft fruit and fresh crisp acidity.

In the U.K.: Corney & Barrow, tel: 020 7265 2400
Private Cellar Ltd., tel: 01353 721999

Château Haut Garrigue

Owner: Sean and Caroline Feely
Winemaker: Sean Feely
Address: Wild Earth Vineyards, 24240 Saussignac
Tel: (0)5 53 22 72 71
Fax: (0)5 53 22 72 71
Email: caroline@wildearthvineyards.com
How to get there: Turn off the D936 at Gardonne by the Renault garage towards Saussignac. After about 4km the road crosses the D14 and starts to climb. About 100m after the crossroads take the left fork signposted Château Haut Garrigue, then the next left just before the cemetery and it is the last property on that road.
Appellations: Bergerac Rouge, Sec; Saussignac
Price: Band B

Vineyard: Two east-facing parcels make up a 14 hectare property with 9.5 hectares under vine of which just over half is planted with red varieties, Merlot accounting for 80% with Cabernet Sauvignon and Cabernet Franc. For the whites, half Sémillon, half Sauvignon, aged about 30 years whilst the reds are a touch older, some up to 50 years old.

Terroir: Clay-limestone soils on a limestone base.

Viticulture: The Feelys use organic practices in the vineyard and the certification process with Ecocert started in 2006. Methods are labour-intensive but they are confident they are creating healthier vines and more flavourful wines from naturally lower yields. Biodynamic preparations like nettle tea are used to stimulate the vines' immune system and vitalise the soils.

Vinification: Old vines and low yields are the key to quality fruit here and there is a minimum interventionist policy in the winery though modern techniques such as cold stabilisation are used. No animal products are used during the winemaking process so the wines are suitable for vegetarians and vegans.

Visits: Open every day with guided tours by appointment. There is a 30-minute way-marked walk round the property. Two-hour wine course also available (see www.frenchwineadventures.com). English and French spoken.

History: The date carved into the stone above the cellar door reads 1737 but it was as recently as 2005 that Caroline and Sean Feely descended on the Dordogne, following their dream to make exclusive organic wines. They turned their backs on the city life and their careers in banking and IT, choosing instead the "wild earth vineyards" of Saussignac. The first year was very hard with Sean suffering two accidents including losing a finger at the start of the 2006 harvest but their passion and determination have kept them going and their wines are selling well.

The Wines: A number of Bergerac Sec cuvées
                   Bergerac Merlot

Comments: The Sauvignon 2006 was fresh and crisp with pronounced grapefruit acidity. The Merlot was deep in colour with rich blackberry fruit, freshness and a bit of grip on the finish. This is a property to keep an eye on for the future.

In the U.K: Consult internet site: www.wildearthvineyards.com for direct deliveries.

Château Lardy

Owner/Winemaker: Emmanuel Vurpillot
Address: 24240 Razac-de-Saussignac
Tel: (0)6 79 71 81 39
Email: manu.vurpillot@wanadoo.fr
How to get there: Leave the D936 at Gardonne,
heading south on the D4, take the first right the D14
then the third left the C204 towards Razac.
Go up the hill to the hamlet of Thenon and after 200m downhill, turn right towards Le Lardy.
Ring the bell at the chai or sound your horn on arrival.
Appellations: Bergerac Rouge, Saussignac
Price: Band A
Vineyard: A family-run property of 15 hectares, of which ten are planted with Merlot, three
with Cabernet Sauvignon and two with white varieties, Sémillon, Muscadelle and Sauvignon
Gris. The vines are all 30 years old with a north-south orientation and sit astride three
appellations including Bordeaux.
Terroir: Superficial stony clay soils on a hard limestone bedrock. Posts can only be sunk in
the ground with the help of a pneumatic drill!
Viticulture: Some plantings are at a density of 5000 to the hectare but there are also some
high vines with 3 metres between rows. Organic herbicides are used for the red grape vines
and the whites are grassed down to encourage the growth of small concentrated bunches.
The vines are trimmed (rognage) as high as possible to maximize exposure to the sun. A
"lutte raisonnée" approach means that spraying is kept to a minimum and in any case stops
3 weeks before harvest to avoid any residues. Yields are low, largely because of the nature
of the terroir, often 17 hl/ha for the Saussignac.
Vinification: The grapes are de-stemmed and a horizontal Vaslin press is used. The juice for
the Saussignac is cold-settled and fermented at no more than 20 degrees before spending a
year in oak. The reds undergo the malolactic fermentation in barrel and are matured in
American oak.
Visits: Every day but preferably at the end of the afternoon. Please ring beforehand. French
and English spoken.
History: The main part of the Château dates from the Middle Ages and at the Revolution, the
owners fled to England to escape the guillotine. It eventually passed to its tenant farmer for
the price of a pair of oxen. The Château was bought in 1932 by Emmanuel's great-
grandfather. From 1995 the family has concentrated on producing wines and Emmanuel,
after studying commerce, took over the running of the property and planted a further ten
hectares of vines. Most sales are to individual customers in France and Belgium. When
Emmanuel is not in the vineyard, he is probably writing or playing music in his rock band.
The Wines: Bergerac Rouge Chêne
                 Saussignac
Comments: Just two wines tasted but both excellent and worth making the trip. The oak-
aged red 2005 was mainly Cabernet Sauvignon so a bit of a rarity in these parts. The
American oak was well-handled imparting discreet tannins and vanilla backed by a dollop of
rich damson and blackcurrant fruit and with a complex nose of cedar, tobacco and coffee.
The Saussignac had a honeyed nose with a hint of tobacco and almonds and a rich medley
of fruits on the palate, bananas, oranges and dried fruits, deliciously sweet but never cloying.
In the U.K.: Not available.

Château la Maurigne

Owner/Winemaker: Chantal & Patrick Gérardin
Address: 24240 Razac de Saussignac
Tel: (0)5 53 27 25 45
Fax: (0)5 53 27 25 45
Email: contact@chateaulamaurigne.com
How to get there: On the hillside between
Razac and Saussignac.
Appellations: Bergerac Rouge, Sec; Côtes de
Bergerac Rouge, Moelleux; Saussignac
Price: Band A/B

Vineyard: 7 hectares of vines on a 17 hectare property, south-facing, planted with Sémillon (70%), Muscadelle (20%) and Sauvignon (10%) and for the reds, Cabernet Franc (60%), Merlot (30%) and Cabernet Sauvignon (10%). The relatively high proportions of Cabernet Franc and Muscadelle are quite unusual. On average the red grape vines are 35 years old and the white varieties 50 years old though some are as old as 70.

Terroir: Very poor clay-limestone soils.

Viticulture: Organic farming with maintenance of hedgerows and protection of flora and fauna. Yields are low, 25-30 hl/ha for the reds, and harvesting is by hand for all the wines. Vines are planted at up to 6000 to the hectare, and grassing down is every other row. The vines are old and resistant to rot and it is usual to spray as little as five times a year. Interestingly, the Gérardins have a donkey which they intend to use in the vineyard whenever possible to avoid compaction of the soil caused by tractors and machinery. Patrick also uses some biodynamic methods, making his own decoctions from laurel and willow which he adds to the Bordeaux mixture.

Vinification: Traditional, with long maceration in oak barrels for the Saussignac, and thereafter 2 to 4 years of oak maturation. The red Côtes de Bergerac also spends 2 years in barrel. The Bergerac Sec is made from Sémillon, Sauvignon and Muscadelle grapes, 20% of which are "passerillés", that is to say they have been allowed to dry on the vines, and this adds exotic fruit flavours. They are left on the fine lees before spending 18 months in oak. Indigenous yeasts are used with minimum use of sulphur. Reds are unfined and unfiltered.

Visits: The vineyard and winery can be visited all year round from 9 a.m. to 7 p.m. French and a little English spoken.

History: The Gerardins bought the vineyard in 1997. The house was built at the beginning of the 16th century on Gallo-Roman fortifications.

The Wines: Bergerac Sec
             Côtes de Bergerac Rouge Cuvée
             Saussignac Château, Cuvée and Florilège

Comments: The Bergerac Sec is pale straw in colour with hints of green, has a honeyed nose and is well-balanced in the mouth with sherbety citrus and green plum flavours, quite intense and with a longish finish. The Côtes de Bergerac was deep in colour, oak still dominating the quite earthy nose and on the palate, intense dark fruit flavours but still marked by tannins which will no doubt soften over the next year or two.

As well as tasting the wines, you can also sample other fruits and discover wild orchids, according to the season.

In the U.K.: Not available.

Clos du Mège

Owner/Winemaker: Helena de Jong

Address: La Bastide, 24240 Monestier

Tel: (0)5 53 58 95 15

Fax: (0)5 53 58 95 15

Email: la.ferme.du.mege@wanadoo.fr

How to get there: From Gardonne take the D4 through Saussignac to Monestier and follow the signs to La Bastide on the road to Cunèges.

Appellations: Bergerac Rouge

Price: Band B

Vineyard: 12 hectare property of which 2.5 are given over to vines. Only red grape varieties are planted namely, Cabernet Sauvignon (60%), Cabernet Franc (20%) and Malbec (20%). Half a hectare has recently been planted with Merlot.

Terroir: Clay-limestone soils.

Viticulture: A traditional approach is adopted in the vineyard with all operations being carried out by hand. The soil is ploughed though there is a certain amount of grassing down. Leaf thinning is not systematic but is done when necessary. A careful selection is made on the vine and at the chai with often 20% of the grapes being rejected. Planting is at 3500 vines to the hectare.

Vinification: Just one red wine is produced here, in stainless steel, though a wooden fermenting vat is to be purchased. Pigeage is done by hand and the wine spends six months in oak. A lot of the production is exported to Holland.

Visits: By arrangement.

History: The vineyard is part of the Ferme du Mège which is a holiday village as well as a farm where you can enjoy a holiday, follow a painting course with artist and sculptor Renépaul Kraeutler and help with the harvest. The holiday bungalows are built in the form of "bories", round dry-stone shepherds' huts typical of the Périgord and Provence.

The Wines: Bergerac Rouge Champ de la Bastide

Comments: Deep rich ruby in colour, there was a hint of liquorice and vanilla on the nose but the palate was dominated by an intensity and freshness of dark fruits.

In the U.K.: Not available.

Château Miaudoux

Owner/Winemaker: Gérard Cuisset
Address: 24240 Saussignac
Tel: (0)5 53 27 92 31
Fax: (0)5 53 27 96 60
Email: Gerard.cuisset@wanadoo.fr
How to get there: Once you are in the village of Saussignac, south of Gardonne, take the road towards Razac-de-Saussignac and after 400m look for a sign on the left to the property.
Appellations: Bergerac Rouge, Sec, Rosé; Côtes de Bergerac; Saussignac
Price: Band B
Vineyard: 27 hectares of which two thirds are planted with white varieties, namely Sémillon, Sauvignon and a little Muscadelle, and the rest with Merlot with some Cabernet Franc and Cabernet Sauvignon. The vines are aged up to 30 years old for the whites, half that for the reds.
Terroir: Clay-limestone with some boulbène.
Viticulture: Organic viticulture certified by Ecocert since 2006. Gérard is a well-respected organic grower, one of the prime movers in the field. There is some natural grassing down and clover is also planted between rows to aerate the soil. An intercep is used to work the soil under the vines, replacing the unpopular work of "décavaillonnage". Planting density is 5000 to the hectare and organic composts are applied when necessary. Yields average 15-20% less than the AOC requirement.
Vinification: The dry whites are macerated on the skins for about 24 hours, cold-settled, with a cool fermentation, in barrique for certain cuvées, and some maturation on the lees with regular stirring and racking. The Saussignac is harvested by hand with 3 or 4 passes and is fermented and aged in oak for up to 18 months.
Visits: Monday to Friday, 10.00 a.m. to 12.00 a.m. and 2.00 p.m. to 6.00 p.m. but please ring beforehand. French and a little English spoken.
History: Gérard Cuisset bought the property in 1991 but had already worked in the vineyard for several years before that. He has gradually increased the size of his holding since then. With his wife Nathalie, he has recently converted to organic viticulture.
The Wines: Bergerac Sec Château Miaudoux
      Bergerac Sec l'Inspiration des Miaudoux
      Côtes de Bergerac Blanc Château Miaudoux
      Saussignac
Comments: We tasted the two "Inspiration" cuvées. The white was rich and buttery with a discreet but obvious oak presence and opinions were divided on this more complex style. Verdict on the red was unequivocal. It had vanilla and forest fruits on the nose, and on the palate smooth mouth-filling flavours of dark fruits, a hint of chocolate and well-integrated tannins.

In the U.K.: The Wine Society, tel: 01438 737700
      Tanners Ltd., tel: 01743 234500
      Nethergate Wines, tel: 01787 283228

Château Monestier la Tour

Owner/Winemaker: Philip de Haseth-Möller
Address: 24240 Monestier
Tel: (0)5 53 24 18 43
Fax: (0)5 53 24 18 14
Email: contact@chateaumonestierlatour.com
How to get there: From Gardonne take the D4 through Saussignac and direction Monestier, looking out for the signs to the domain.
Appellations: Bergerac Rouge, Sec, Rosé; Côtes de Bergerac; Saussignac
Price: Band B/C
Vineyard: 33 hectares situated on the gentle slopes of Monestier and Thénac and planted with Sémillon (50%), Sauvignon (40%) and Muscadelle (10%) for the whites, Merlot (60%), Cabernets (35%) and Malbec (5%) for the reds. The vines are 20 to 25 years old on average.
Terroir: Clay-limestone soils
Viticulture: A "lutte raisonnée" approach is adopted with minimal intervention and moves are being made towards organic certification. Vines are planted at 5000 to the hectare and the space between rows is grassed down or planted with cereals when appropriate. Leaf thinning takes places on the eastern side for the reds and green harvesting is practised as and when necessary. Yields are 35-45 hl/ha.
Vinification: The grapes are carefully sorted and small tanks are used so that each parcel can be vinified separately. Indigenous yeasts are used and the reds undergo a maceration of up to 20 days after the slow alcoholic fermentation, with the malolactic taking place in tank or barrique depending on the cuvée. The reds are neither fined nor filtered. The whites are macerated on the skins and there is some fermentation in oak with time on the fine lees.
Visits: Monday to Friday, from 8.30 a.m. to 12.00 a.m. and 2.00 p.m. to 5.00 p.m. French and English spoken.
History: Bought by Dutch businessman Philip de Haseth-Möller in 1998, the Château has been superbly renovated and the same detail has been brought to the vineyard with the collaboration of renowned consultant oenologist Stéphane Derenoncourt. The Château dates back to the 13th century but was partly destroyed during the Hundred Years War. There were some additions during the Renaissance period, the façade was rebuilt in the 17th century and the tower in the nineteenth.
The Wines: Tour de Monestier Rouge and Blanc
Château Monestier la Tour Rouge and Blanc
Côtes de Bergerac Rouge Cuvée Emily
Comments: The Château Bergerac Rouge had a toasted oaky nose with hints of smoke and tar. There was rich blackcurrant fruit with discreet tannins and a longish finish. The Côtes "Emily" had seen more new oak and was from lower yields and there was a definite step up in quality. Smoke and spicy fruit aromas led on to warm satisfying black fruit flavours with well-integrated tannins, no hard edges, and a long smoky finish.

In the U.K.: Corney and Barrow, tel: 020 72652400

Château de Panisseau

Owner/Winemaker: Daniel Evrard & Bernadette Gaspard
Address: 24240 Thénac
Tel: (0)5 53 58 40 03
Fax: (0)5 53 58 04 46
Email: panisseau@ifrance.com
How to get there: Take the D17 out of Sigoulès, take a right turn towards Thénac and look for a sign on your right.
Appellations: Bergerac Rouge, Sec, Rosé; Côtes de Bergerac

Vineyard: 75 hectares, of which 61% are planted with red grape varieties and 39% white. The vineyards are planted on well-drained hillsides overlooking the château. Average age of the white grape varieties is 33 years, the oldest dating from 1930 and the average for the reds is 20 years, going back to 1965.

Terroir: The white grape varieties are planted on heavier clayey sand and silts, the Cabernets and Malbec on the chalky soils and Merlot on the heavy clayey silt and silica, always with a chalky subsoil. The presence of silica is quite rare in the appellation and adds an element of finesse to the wines. Recent planting has been high density (6500 vines per hectare).

Viticulture: Since Belgian couple Daniel and Bernadette took over in 1999, yields have been reduced considerably to a global figure of 30 hl/ha for the reds and 38 hl/ha for the whites., the best vintages yielding only 20 hl/ha. This is due to severe crop thinning in July and the grapes are brought to optimum maturity by careful leaf thinning. The best parcels are picked by hand and the property is run on "lutte raisonnée" lines.

Vinification: The grapes are sorted by hand and all pumps have been replaced by conveyor belts to avoid bruising the grapes and to preserve the aromas. Fermentation is temperature controlled, punching down is done automatically and the chai is equipped with micro-oxygenation equipment. Whites are matured on the lees, some in barrel, and the reds are matured in oak, the length of time depending on the cuvée. None of the wines are filtered.

Visits: Reception is open for sales from Monday to Saturday.

History: The castle was built by the British at the time of the fourth crusade, a little before 1200. Its architecture was revised somewhat during the Renaissance but it remains a fine example of a medieval Périgord château and has been carefully maintained by a succession of owners. It was bought by Belgian couple Daniel Evrard and Bernadette Gaspard in 1999 and with the help of consultant oenologist Jean-Marc Dournel, they are again producing wines of great quality as highlighted by a string of awards and recommendations in the wine press.

The Wines: Panisseau produces a whole range of wines from entry level upwards, including sparkling wines.

> Bergerac Blanc sec "Divin"
> Côtes de Bergerac Rouge "Baccarat"

Comments: The "Divin" is a third each of Sauvignon, Sémillon and Muscadelle, with the added complexity of 10 months in oak. The "Baccarat" is Merlot dominated and unfiltered, after 18 months in new oak. We tasted the Bergerac Sec Alcea which had a honeyed pineapple nose, good weight in the mouth from 80% Sémillon, good soft fruit and acidity balance and a medium finish.

In the U.K.: Not available

Château le Payral

Owner/Winemaker: Isabelle & Thierry Daulhiac
Address: 24240 Razac-de-Saussignac
Tel: (0)5 53 22 38 07
Fax: (0)5 53 27 99 81
Email: daulhiac.thierry@wanadoo.fr
How to get there: South of Gardonne which is on the D936 between Bergerac and Ste Foy la Grande. Make for Razac and follow the signs to the property which is on the other side of the road to the Route des Vins sign.
Appellations: Bergerac, Côtes de Bergerac, Saussignac
Price: Band A/B
Vineyard: 15 ha of vines which are 20 years old on the south bank of the Dordogne. Eight hectares are for white wine production, namely Sémillon, Sauvignon and Muscadelle, and seven for red with Merlot, Cabernet Sauvignon and Cabernet Franc.
Terroir: Clay-limestone soils.
Viticulture: Thierry has followed "lutte raisonnée" principles for a number of years and is now organic since 2005. Planting density is 5000 to 5500 vines to the hectare with a mixture of high and low vines. Soils are ploughed in the spring and every other row is grassed down. Green harvesting takes place as necessary and yields are kept to 55 hl/ha for the dry whites and 40 to 50 for the reds. Harvesting is by machine except of course for the Saussignac. Every effort has been made to match terroir and vines.
Vinification: The whites are matured on the lees whilst the Saussignac is fermented and aged in oak. The reds have an initial cool maceration of one week, fermentation in open vats with regular "pigeage" but no pumping over. Micro-oxygenation is sometimes used with the reds.
Visits: Monday to Saturday, 9.00 a.m. to 12.00 a.m. and 2.00 p.m. to 7.00 p.m. French and English spoken.
History: Thierry took over the domain from his father in 1992 after the property had been purchased by the family around 1970. Following the example of his brother-in-law Gérard Cuisset of Château Miaudoux, Thierry now bottles his own production.
The Wines: The Saussignac liquoreux is available in a number of vintages dating back several years.

> Bergerac Terres Rouges Merlot
> Bergerac Sec

Comments: The Bergerac Sec was a good example with a fresh floral nose and hints of citrus and gooseberry fruit. It had a softness in the mouth, a hint of tropical fruit with crisp and clean acidity. Bright gold in colour, the Saussignac 2003 had an intriguing nose of clean linen, flowers and marzipan with a richness of honeyed raisin fruit and memories of buttercup syrup, shot through with a streak of acidity which created a wonderful balance.
The domain also offers chambres d'hôte in the heart of the vineyard, available during the summer.

In the U.K.: Enotria Winecellars, tel: 020 8961 4411

Château Perrou

Owner/Winemaker: Yves d'Amécourt
Address: 24240 Gageac et Rouillac
Tel: (0)5 56 71 54 56
Fax: (0)5 56 71 83 95
Email: vignesdamecourt@aol.com
How to get there: The chai is on the D14, a couple of kilometres on the Monbazillac side of La Ferrière.
Appellations: Bergerac, Monbazillac, Saussignac
Price: Band B

Vineyard: Quite a large property of 74 hectares planted with Merlot (50%), Cabernet Sauvignon (30%), Cabernet Franc (18%), with a little Malbec and some remaining Fer Servadou. For the whites, 70% Sauvignon, 28% Sémillon and a little Muscadelle and Ugni Blanc. The vines average 50 years old for the reds and 30 for the whites.

Terroir: This is probably the only property with parcels in both the sweet white appellations of Saussignac and Monbazillac. The Saussignac terroir comprises a south-facing plateau of Castillon limestone and clay-limestone slopes facing the Dordogne with the valley of the Gardonnette to the west. The Monbazillac parcels are clay soils with flint, planted in clearings in the woods within the commune of Pomport.

Viticulture: Yves is an enthusiastic advocate of planting wide and high. His vines are planted in rows 3 metres apart and he prefers to see planting density simply as one factor amongst many to consider, rather than the be all and end all. Wide planting does allow for rapid harvesting by machine, less use of pesticides and weed-killers if grassing down, less use of fuel for tractors. It is important, however, to restrict yields per vine, finding a balance that produces good quality fruit but is economically viable.

Vinification: The reds undergo a cool maceration before being fermented at quite a low temperature. A pneumatic press is used with successive rackings to clarify the wine and avoid the need for too much filtration. They are aged for 18 months in tank and barrel. The sweet whites are vinified and matured in 500 litre demi-muids, the oak being a mixture of French and American. Maître de chai is Karine Dumonteil.

Visits: It is best to ring first. French, English, German and Spanish spoken.

History: The d'Amécourt family can trace its noble ancestry back to the Crusades. As the de Ponton d'Amécourts they somehow survived the Revolution and Charles-François was made baron in 1811 and fought with Napoleon at Moscow. The best cuvées are named after the Marquis de Lentilhac, an uncle of the d'Amécourts, from a family which played an important rôle in the history of the Périgord in the Middle Ages. The Château de Perrou itself is some way from the chai. Yves d'Amécourt bought the property in 2002. He is based in Sauveterre-de-Guyenne and also has properties in Bordeaux including Château Bellevue.

The Wines: Saussignac, Monbazillac, Bergerac Marquis de Lentilhac

Comments: Pick of the reds, not surprisingly perhaps, was the 2005 with its warm black fruits and touch of spice and liquorice. It was interesting to taste both the Monbazillac and the Saussignac. The former was honey and almonds with beeswax on the nose and relatively light in style. The Saussignac, less spirity than some, had excellent balance of candied fruits and sugars.

In the U.K.: Not available.

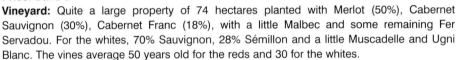

Château Richard

Owner/winemaker: Richard Doughty
Address: 24240 Monestier
Tel: (0)5 53 58 49 13 **Fax:** (0)5 53 58 49 30
Email: info@chateaurichard.com
How to get there: Situated on the D4 between Saussignac and Couture.
Appellations: Bergerac Rouge, Sec and Rosé, Saussignac
Price: Band B
Vineyard: About 17 ha on hillsides and plateau. The vines are on average 26 years old for the reds and 44 years old for the whites, with the oldest planted in 1932.
Terroir: Soils are shallow on limestone and molasse.
Viticulture: The vineyard is organic, certified by Ecocert. No chemical pesticides or fertilisers are used. The rows are ploughed and the work in the vineyard is done by hand rather than by machine whenever possible, including pruning and harvesting.
Vinification: For the Saussignac, native yeasts are used and the fermentation can last until July. Old oak barrels are used, usually 500 litres, so as not to have too much influence on the wine. It is a blend of Sémillon, Sauvignon and Muscadelle with variations between the different cuvées but always with the Muscadelle playing an important role. The wine is aged in oak for up to four years, in the case of the Grand Coup de Coeur.
Richard believes in taking a few risks in the pursuit of good wine and his Bergerac Rouge Cuvée Osée/Osons is interesting as it is made without any additives, no chaptalisation, and most importantly, no use of SO2 at any stage. It is matured for 3 months in old barrels with no racking during this period and is bottled without fining or filtration.
Visits: Monday to Friday, 9.30 a.m. to 12.30 p.m. and 2.00 p.m. to 7.00 p.m. French and English spoken.
History: A larger than life character, Richard Doughty has an English father and a French mother. After a career in oceanography, a parachuting accident led eventually to his training in viticulture and oenology in Sauternes and his purchase in 1987 of his present estate. Richard is a committed ecologist and has been a leading player in the promotion of organic wine production in the area, having been President of the Syndicat des vins bio d'Aquitaine for several years.
The Wines: Various cuvées of Saussignac, in particular the Cuvée Noble, Coup de Coeur and Grand Coup de Coeur. Of special interest is the Bergerac Rouge Cuvée Osée/Osons (Daring Cuvée!) made without any addition of SO2 at any stage.
Comments: Richard seems to have changed the name of the Cuvée slightly from Osée to Osons but the result appears to be much the same, a deep dense garnet in the glass, hints of charring, liquorice and autumn leaves on the nose, and in the mouth, deep berry flavours with a touch of dark chocolate and a good dry finish. An individual wine of some character.
The Saussignac Cuvée Noble was light straw in colour with hints of green, lighter and fresher in style than many with a good balance between sweetness and acidity. Would go well with fruit desserts or as an apéritif.
In the U.K.: Vintage Roots: 01189 761999
Ballantyne's of Cowbridge: 02920 222202

Château le Tap

Owner/Winemaker: Olivier Roches

Address: 24240 Saussignac

Tel: (0)5 53 27 53 41

Fax: (0)5 53 22 07 55

Email: chateauletap@tiscali.fr

How to get there: Turn off the D936 at Gardonne by the Renault garage towards Saussignac. After about 4 km the road crosses the D14 and starts to climb. About 100m after the crossroads take the left fork and follow the signs.

Appellations: Saussignac; Bergerac Rouge, Sec; Côtes de Bergerac Rouge, Moelleux

Price: Band B

Vineyard: Almost 14 hectares planted with Merlot and Cabernet Sauvignon for the reds, Sémillon, Sauvignon and Muscadelle for the white, the vines being 35 years old on average.

Terroir: Clay-limestone and stony soils.

Viticulture: Olivier has a "lutte raisonnée" approach with short pruning and total grassing down on some parcels. He is moving towards organic viticulture and has cut copper treatments by two thirds and only uses organic fertilizers. Yields are kept to 40-45 hl/ha and harvesting is by hand for the moelleux and of course the Saussignac. Grapes for the dry whites are harvested at night. Olivier is currently replanting 3 hectares at a density of 5000 vines to the hectare.

Vinification: The Bergerac Sec grapes are macerated on the skins for about 30 hours in the case of the Sauvignon and slightly longer for the Sémillon. Reds are macerated about 30 days with "remontage" and "délestage" to enhance extraction. Micro-oxygenation during fermentation is used for the easy-drinking reds. The Saussignac is fermented in barrel and is aged for a further year in oak. Stainless steel tanks are used for fermentation and cement vats for maturation.

Visits: Monday to Saturday, 8.00 a.m. to 12.00 a.m. and 2.00 p.m. to 7.00 p.m. French, English and German spoken.

History: Olivier is the son of Michel Roches and brother of Didier at Domaine du Haut Pécharmant, a fifth generation winemaker. He started at Le Tap in 2000 since when he has rebuilt the winery and created a gîte with swimming pool.

The Wines: Bergerac Sec Cuvée Grand Chêne
Saussignac
Bergerac Rouge Cuvée Julie Jolie

Comments: The 2005 Saussignac had a honeyed nose but was clean and fresh, rich and opulent with good length. Julie Jolie was more than just a pretty face! It had a perfumed floral nose, rich blackberry and plum fruit in the mouth, balanced by soft tannins and oaky vanillas. Outstandingly good.

In the U.K.: Not available.

Château des Vigiers

Owner/Winemaker: SCEA de la Font du Roc

Address: 24240 Monestier

Tel: (0)5 53 61 50 30

Fax: (0)5 53 61 50 31

Email: vigiers@vigiers.com

How to get there: Take the D936 west from Bergerac as far as Gardonne, then turn left on the D4 , through Saussignac and follow the signs.

Appellations: Bergerac Rouge, Sec, Rosé; Côtes de Bergerac

Price: Band B

Vineyard: 17 hectares of which 11 are planted with red varieties and 6 with white. For the reds, Merlot (31%), Cabernet Franc (33%), Cabernet Sauvignon (33%), Malbec (3%). White varieties are Sauvignon (70%), Sémillon (20%) and Muscadelle (10%). The vines average 20 years of age.

Terroir: Mainly clay-limestone.

Viticulture: "Lutte raisonnée" approach, using organic fertilisers. Planting density is around 4000 vines to the hectare with 10 to 14 buds being left on each vine. Every other row is grassed down. Leaf thinning is done by hand about a month before harvest and yields are about 38 hl/ha for both reds and whites.

Vinification: The dry whites have a pre-fermentation maceration on the skins and the Cuvée Elisabeth is fermented in new oak barrels, followed by a further eight months maturation in French oak with lees stirring. The reds have a 30 day cuvaison with temperature controlled at 25-30 deg. The Côtes de Bergerac spends 12 to 16 months in new French oak which comes from Nevers, Allier and the Vosges and is medium toasted.

Visits: Tastings take place in the brasserie which is open every day from 12.00 a.m. to 4.00 p.m. and 7.00 p.m. to 10.00 p.m.

History: The Château was the work of Jean Vigier, judge to the king in Ste Foy la Grande, who undertook its construction in 1597. Four centuries later, in 1989, the Château was bought and renovated by Lars Urban Petersson and his wife Elisabeth. It was converted into a four-star hotel complex with golf courses and restaurants.

The Wines: Bergerac Sec Cuvée Elisabeth
Côtes de Bergerac Cuvée Jean Vigier

Comments: It is well worth making a visit to Château des Vigiers to enjoy lunch in the brasserie in beautiful surroundings, perhaps take in a round of golf, or treat yourself to a few nights at the hotel. The wines are pretty decent too. The red Cuvée Jean Vigier we tasted was the 1999 which had retained a lot of colour but was beginning to look more brick red. There was oak evident on the nose with spice and leather and although the fruit was beginning to fade, there was a smoothness and complexity that were quite pleasing.

In the U.K: Not available

Clos d'Yvigne

Owner/Winemaker: Patricia Atkinson
Address: 24240 Gageac et Rouillac
Tel: (0)5 53 22 94 40
Email: patricia.atkinson@wanadoo.fr
How to get there: Take the D933 towards Mont de Marsan and after 2 or 3 kilometres, turn right on the valley road, the D14 until you see the sign for Gageac et Rouillac. Continue up the hill towards the Château and the church. Clos d'Yvigne is opposite the church.
Appellations: Bergerac, Saussignac
Price: Band C
Vineyard: 21 hectares planted with Merlot, Cabernet Sauvignon and Cabernet Franc, Sauvignon, Sémillon and Muscadelle. White grape vines average 15 years of age, the reds much older at about 50. The vineyard lies on the beautiful ridge of hills to the south of the river.
Terroir: A mix of clay and gravel on a limestone base.
Viticulture: Severe pruning in winter and spring reduces yields. Careful husbandry in the vineyard, a "lutte raisonnée" approach to the use of chemicals and natural farming methods lead to healthy fruit. Some gobelet training for the Saussignac. Low yields of 15 hl/ha for the Saussignac and 35-40 hl/ha for the reds. Planting density 5000-6000 vines to the hectare.
Vinification: The dry whites benefit from overnight maceration and the Cuvée Nicholas is fermented and aged for nine months in oak, half of which is new. The reds have a long maceration period to extract maximum fruit, colour and tannins. Both reds are aged in oak for 18 months to 2 years. The Saussignac is made from noble rot affected grapes, after six or seven separate picks. It is fermented in oak and spends up to three years in oak depending on its evolution in barrel.
Visits: Monday to Friday, 9.00 a.m. to 12.00 a.m. and 2.00 p.m. to 5.00 p.m. It is best to ring first. English and French spoken.
History: Patricia bought the vineyard with 4 hectares in 1989 and neighbouring vines in 1995, as is well documented in her best-selling book "The Ripening Sun". It has been a dream come true but not without a huge amount of hard work and a burning desire to be successful and to be accepted in the local winemaking fraternity. I suggest you read the book before you visit, it will mean so much more.
The Wines: As an accomplished writer as well as winemaker, Patricia has given a literary theme to her different cuvées.

> Bergerac Sec Princesse de Clèves / Bergerac Sec Cuvée Nicholas
> Côtes de Bergerac Le Rouge et le Noir / Côtes de Bergerac Le Petit Prince
> Bergerac Rosé Bel Ami / Saussignac

Comments: The Cuvée Nicholas had a fresh nose of citrus fruits and flowers, it filled the mouth with intense grapefruit and gooseberry flavours with a touch of oak complexity and crisp refreshing acidity. Le Petit Prince 2005 had complex aromas of black fruits, liquorice, tobacco and chocolate, deep brambly fruit with a nice bit of grip on the finish and the tannins and structure to last a while yet. The Saussignac was definitely liquoreux in style with a hint of spearmint, coconut and ginger on the nose, opulent honey and peach fruit and a streak of acidity.
In the U.K.: Majestic Wines, tel: 0845 605 6767, John Avery's of Bristol, tel: 0845 863 0995 and Justerini and Brooks, tel: 020 7484 6400

Montravel

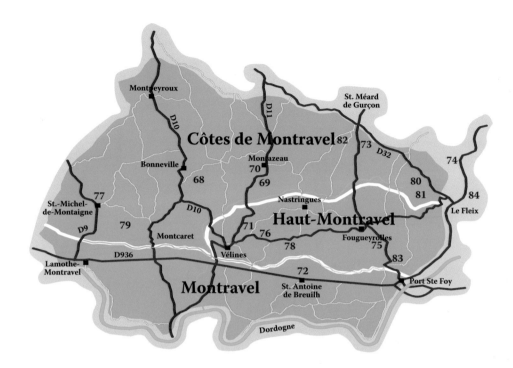

68.
*Château
du Bloy*

69.
*Château Brunet
Charpentière*

70.
*Domaine de
Grimardy*

71.
Jonc-Blanc

72.
*Château
Julien*

73.
*Château
Laulerie*

74.
*Château de la
Mallevieille*

75.
*Château
Masburel*

76.
*Château
Masmontet*

77.
*Château Michel
de Montaigne*

78.
*Château
Moulin Caresse*

79.
*Château
Moulin Garreau*

80.
*Château
Pique-Segue*

81.
*Château
Puy-Servain*

82.
*Château
le Raz*

83.
*Château la
Ressaudie*

84.
*Union Vinicole
Bergerac-Le Fleix*

Château du Bloy

Owner/Winemaker: Olivier Lambert &
Bertrand Lepoittevin-Dubost

Address: Le Blois, 24230 Bonneville
Tel: (0)5 53 22 47 87
Fax: (0)5 53 27 56 34
Email: chateau.du.bloy@wanadoo.fr

How to get there: From Bergerac take the
D936 towards Castillon, turning off at
Vélines. Follow the road to Bonneville and
look for the signs for the domain.

Appellations: Bergerac, Côtes de Bergerac, Montravel

Price: Band B

Vineyard: 20 hectares on the right bank of the Dordogne with some parcels on the slopes of varying expositions. 15 ha are planted with red varieties: 50% Merlot, 35% Cabernet Franc, 15% Cabernet Sauvignon. For the whites, 54% Sauvignon, 33% Sémillon, 13% Muscadelle. Vines are 30 years old, planted at 3300 to 5000 vines to the hectare.

Terroir: Clay and fine silt.

Viticulture: "Lutte raisonnée" approach with use of organic fertilisers, de-budding and leaf thinning by hand, green harvesting if necessary. Average yields of just 35 hl/ha. Grassing down is practised although after problems in the heatwave of 2003 when the vineyard was totally grassed down, this is now restricted to every other row.

Vinification: The reds have a cuvaison of 3 to 6 weeks, depending on the vintage, with pre-fermentation maceration. Top cuvées spend from 12 to 16 months in oak. Temperature-controlled fermentation for the whites after short maceration on the skins. Indigenous yeasts are used. "Le Bloy" range is fermented and matured in barriques. The château has the services of oenologists Marc Quertinier and Julien Belle.

Visits: Monday to Friday, 8.00 a.m. to 12.00 a.m. and 2.00 p.m. to 6.00 p.m. French, English and Spanish spoken.

History: The property exists in its present form since the early sixties though it was already mentioned in the 1903 Féret guide. In 2001 it was acquired by Olivier and Bertrand, formerly computer engineer and corporate lawyer respectively, their aim to make it one of the best domains in the south-west. They would seem to be well on the way to doing so, judging by the number of awards received and recommendations in the wine press.

The Wines: Montravel Blanc Sec "Le Bloy"
Bergerac Rouge "Sirius"
Montravel Rouge "Le Bloy"

Comments: The Bergerac Rouge "Sirius" 2003 was ageing gracefully. It had retained its colour and had rich, dark fruit flavours with a ripeness and freshness that were most appealing, balanced by soft velvety tannins.

In the U.K.: Not available.

Château Brunet Charpentière

Owner/Winemaker: Franck Descoins

Address: Les Charpentières, 24230 Montazeau

Tel: (0)5 53 27 54 71

Fax: (0)5 53 27 54 71

Email: franck.descoins@free.fr

How to get there: From Vélines take the D11 to Montazeau and look out for the signs as you approach the village.

Appellations: Bergerac, Côtes de Bergerac, Montravel

Price: Band A

Vineyard: The vineyard of 22 hectares was planted in 1986 with Merlot (70%), Cabernet Sauvignon (20%), and Cabernet Franc (10%) and for the whites, Sémillon (60%), Sauvignon (35%) and Muscadelle (5%).

Terroir: The vines are planted on gentle slopes, south-facing, with clay-limestone soils, with ten hectares on the Montazeau plateau.

Viticulture: Fourteen hectares are still at 3300 vines to the hectare with more recent plantings at 5000. The soil is ploughed with no use of chemical weed-killers and every other row is grassed down. Leaf thinning takes place if necessary, harvesting is by machine with yields of 40-50 hl/ha.

Vinification: For the white Montravel, cool maceration is followed by temperature-controlled fermentation and some lees ageing. The vats are variously of concrete, glass fibre and stainless steel. The red Côtes de Bergerac is aged in French oak barriques, of which 70% are new.

Visits: Every day but it is advisable to ring beforehand.

History: The Descoins have been at the château for over twenty years now and have completely restored the chai in an old barn. They have a loyal clientèle with a third of the production being sold at the cellar.

The Wines: Bergerac Rosé
                    Bergerac Sec
                    Bergerac Rouge
                    Côtes de Bergerac Rouge

Comments: The Bergerac Sec was a real star. Pale lemon in colour with a nose of flowers, gooseberries and nettles, this is a crisp Sauvignon-dominated white with clean refreshing fruit and zingy acidity.

In the U.K.: Not available

Domaine de Grimardy

Owner/Winemaker: Marielle & Marcel Establet

Address: Les Grimards, 24230 Montazeau

Tel: (0)5 53 57 96 78

Fax: (0)5 53 61 97 16

Email: grimardy@wanadoo.fr

How to get there: On the D936 between Castillon-la-Bataille and Ste-Foy-la-Grande, turn towards Vélines at the Les Réaux roundabout. Montazeau is some 5 km. after Vélines in the direction of Montpon. Follow the signs for the domain.

Appellations: Bergerac Rouge, Rosé; Montravel Rouge, Blanc; Vin de Pays du Périgord

Price: Band A/B

Vineyard: 12 hectares of vines aged 30-35 years on average, planted with Merlot (65%), Cabernet Sauvignon (30%), and Cabernet Franc (5%) for the reds, Sémillon (50%) and Sauvignon (50%).

Terroir: Clay-limestone and flinty soils and marl with fossilised oysters.

Viticulture: The soil is hoed beneath the vines and grassed down between the rows. A "lutte raisonnée" approach has been in place since 2000 with no use of chemical pesticides or fertilisers. Following analyses, organic fertiliser is used every other year. Leaves are removed on one side of the vines, facing the rising sun. Grapes for the red Montravel are harvested by hand, the rest mechanically. All grapes are completely de-stemmed.

Vinification: For the dry whites, there is a 24-hour maceration before pressing to allow the varietal aromas to develop. Fermentation and cuvaison for the reds last at least 4 weeks, each variety being vinified separately and assembled after the malolactic fermentation. The Cuvée Marie-Juliette white is matured on its fine lees in barriques. For the Montravel Rouge, maturation is in new oak barrels of 300 litres for 16 to 20 months, the malolactic taking place in barrel.

Visits: Monday to Friday, 9.00 a.m. to 12.00 a.m. and 2.00 p.m. to 7.00 p.m. Weekends by arrangement. French and a little English spoken.

History: Marielle and Marcel took over the property in 1998, having been winemakers in the Bordeaux region. They built the winery from scratch as the previous owners had sent their grapes to the co-operative. They are fifth generation winemakers.

The Wines: Montravel Sec Cuvée Marie-Juliette
Bergerac Rouge fût de Chêne
Montravel Rouge Révélation

Comments: The Marie-Juliette was deep lemon in colour, a delicate nose of honeyed pineapple leading on to quite a complex cocktail of soft fruit flavours with fresh acidity to provide balance. Just taking on some brick red colour, the 2003 Montravel Révélation had pleasant aromas of mocha, liquorice and tobacco and great depth of black fruit flavours superbly balanced by soft tannins. A fine tribute to the appellation!

In the U.K: Not available.

Jonc-Blanc

Owner/Winemaker: Isabelle Carles
& Franck Pascal
Address: 24230 Vélines
Tel: (0)5 53 74 18 97
Fax: (0)5 53 74 18 97
Email: jonc.blanc@free.fr
How to get there: Between Ste-Foy-la-Grande and Castillon-la-Bataille on the D936, turn towards Vélines at the roundabout at les Réaux. As you come out of Vélines, take the 2nd road on the left.
Appellations: Bergerac Rouge, Rosé; Montravel Rouge, Blanc Sec
Price: Band B
Vineyard: 15 hectares of which 12 are given over to red wine production. The vines average 15 years old for the reds and twice that for the whites. The estate is planted with Merlot 45%, Cabernet Sauvignon 45% and Malbec 10%; Sauvignon 70%, Sémillon 25% and Muscadelle 5%.
Terroir: Shallow stony clay-limestone soils.
Viticulture: Under the leadership of Isabelle and Franck, the domain has moved from "lutte raisonnée" to an organic approach with biodynamic principles used on certain parcels. The land is ploughed or left grassed down and other crops such as cereals and vegetables are sown between rows.
Vinification: The emphasis here is very much on producing a natural product. Chaptalisation is not practised, only natural yeasts are used and maturation on the fine lees takes place over a period of 12 to 36 months without any use of sulphur. Some cuvées are aged in oak, 15 to 20% new, and some in 100 year old barrels holding up to 5000 litres, brought from Alsace.
Visits: By arrangement. French, English and German spoken.
History: The domain was mentioned in the Féret guide of 1903 and was bought by the present owners in 2000. Franck and Isabelle have established a reputation for producing fruit-driven natural wines, perhaps less complex than some of their neighbours' wines, but expressive of their terroir. In just five years, they have obtained 8 gold medals and 5 silver at the Wine Fairs of Paris, Bordeaux and Macon, and the wine press has been more than complimentary. They have recently decided to drop the "château" from their label and replace it with the words "paysans vignerons" to emphasise their passion and devotion to the land.
The Wines: Le Sens du Fruit
Coup de Foudre/Coeur de Foudre
Cuvée Rubis
Comments: With its youthful glossy blueberry colour, the Coeur de Foudre 2005, marketed as a vin de table, had a whiff of the farmyard and deep intense blackcurrant flavours with a firm tannic finish that was crying out for some equally robust food. The Montravel Le Rubis showed a bit more complexity with tobacco and tar on the nose and big fruit flavours and well-balanced tannins. These wines really do taste natural, they are honest and straightforward and would go well with the local game or duck magret.
In the U.K.:   Imperial Wine Co. Ltd., tel: 01986 89 29 11

Château Julien

Owner/Winemaker: Viviane Sroka

Address: 24230 St Antoine de Breuilh

Tel: (0)6 16 65 13 67

Fax: (0)5 53 27 82 07

Email: vitijul@club-internet.fr

How to get there: Arriving from Bordeaux on the D936, at the roundabout at the entrance to St Antoine, follow the signs to the property.

Appellations: Bergerac Rouge, Rosé; Montravel Rouge

Price: Band B

Vineyard: Just 3 hectares planted with red varieties only, Merlot (50%), Cabernet Franc (45%) and Cabernet Sauvignon (5%). Vines are 5 years old except on a parcel in the Montravel appellation where the vines are 20 years old.

Terroir: Soils are clay and gravel or gravel on the plain, with clay-limestone in Montravel.

Viticulture: Viviane follows organic procedures, certified Agriculture Biologique. No chemical pesticides, fertilisers or weed-killers are used, the soils are ploughed and all green harvesting is done by hand whether it be de-budding, leaf plucking or bunch thinning. All harvesting is by hand, the grapes are carefully sorted and kept intact in 7-8 kilo baskets.

Vinification: Grapes are de-stemmed and crushed with a 4 to 5 day cool maceration before fermentation is allowed to start naturally. Colour and tannins are extracted by manual pigeage and cuvaison lasts about a month, with some cuvées being matured in oak.

Visits: Please contact by telephone. French, English and German spoken.

History: Viviane came from Alsace where she was in the hotel-restaurant trade and with her husband and son Julien who qualified in Viticulture and Oenology and worked briefly at Château Richard, settled in the Dordogne and planted the vineyard in 2000 in the Montravel area. They are confirmed organic producers and are moving towards bio-dynamism.

The Wines: Clos Julien
Extravagance
Naturellement
Montravel Rouge

Comments: The three Bergerac reds are all 50/50 Merlot and Cabernet Franc. The Naturellement wine has no added sulphur and along with the Montravel spends 18 months in oak. We tasted the Extravagance which had spicy redcurrant and cassis on the nose with an intensity and purity of dark fruits, well-rounded and fresh with soft tannins.

In the U.K.: Not available.

Château Laulerie

Owner/Winemaker: Dubard family
Address: Le Gouyat, 24610 St Méard-de-Gurçon
Tel: (0)5 53 82 48 31 **Fax:** (0)5 53 82 47 64
Email: vignobles-dubard@wanadoo.fr
How to get there: From St Méard-de-Gurçon, take
the D32 towards Le Fleix, take a right turn towards
Ponchapt and look out for the sign.
Appellations: Bergerac Rouge, Sec, Rosé;
Montravel, Côtes de Montravel
Price: Band B
Vineyard: 85 ha. on the right bank of the Dordogne,
overlooking the Estrop, planted with Sauvignon and Sémillon in equal proportions for the
whites, Merlot (60%), Cabernet Sauvignon (15%), Cabernet Franc (15%), Malbec (10%) for
the reds. Overall 60% is planted with red grapes, the remainder with white. The vines are 25
years old on average.
Terroir: Typical of the Montravel area, clay and limestone with some sandy and siliceous soils.
Viticulture: Vines are planted low and in narrow rows at 5000 vines to the hectare. "Lutte
raisonnée" principles are followed. Alternate rows are grassed down or ploughed and
canopy management and green harvesting are also important.
Vinification: For the dry whites, there is a 12-hour cold maceration with slow fermentation in
stainless steel. The Comtesse de Ségur is racked into oak barrels and left on the lees for a
few months. For the reds, there is regular pumping over and délestage (rack and return) for
a progressive extraction of phenolic structure from the grapes. There is some oak ageing in
barrels for up to 12 months. A number of the reds are fermented at relatively low
temperatures to retain fruit flavours and elegance.
Visits: 8.00 a.m. to 12.30 p.m. and 2.00 p.m. to 7.00 p.m. Groups by arrangement. French
and English spoken.
History: The family holding comprises two adjacent properties, Domaine du Gouyat
purchased in 1977 and Château Laulerie which was acquired in 1986. Wines are sold under
both labels. The chai is of typical Périgord architecture, its dovecot being particularly pleasing
to the eye. The barrel store features a "prehistoric" fresco created by local English artist Peter
Thomas. A similar design adorns the bottles of the "Indian Summer" range of varietals. In
2000, the Dubard family also purchased Château les Farcies du Pech in Pécharmant, where
in addition to making wine, the delightful 18th century chartreuse has been converted into 5
chambres d'hôte.
The Wines: Montravel Cuvée Comtesse de Ségur Rouge and Sec
Bergerac Le Raisin and La Cuvée
Pécharmant Château les Farcies du Pech
Domaine du Gouyat Montravel Sec
Comments: Try the Domaine du Gouyat Montravel Sec. I thought the Sauvignon/Sémillon
balance was spot on, fresh and clean but with a soft fruitiness. The Comtesse de Ségur had
a honeyed nose with more complexity but remained fresh and clean. One of my favourites
from the region, however, is the red Comtesse de Ségur with its powerful red fruits, spicy,
silky tannins and some complexity. Don't overlook "Le Raisin", straightforward but with
appealing spicy fruit and "La Cuvée", with a nose of cedar, smoke and chocolate and rich
intense fruits on the palate. Both fine examples of the appellation.
In the U.K: Oxford Wine Co., tel: 01865 301144, Whitebridge Wines, tel: 01785 817229

Château de la Mallevieille

Owner/Winemaker: Philippe Biau & Thierry Bernardinis
Address: 24130 Monfaucon
Tel: (0)5 53 24 64 66 **Fax:** (0)5 53 58 69 91
Email: chateaudelamallevieille@wanadoo.fr
How to get there: Monfaucon is situated just east of St Méard-de-Gurçon and north of Le Fleix. The property is by the side of the D20 Le Fleix to Mussidan road.
Appellations: Bergerac Sec, Rouge, Rosé; Montravel Sec, Rouge, Haut-Montravel; Côtes de Bergerac Rouge, Moelleux
Price: Band B/C
Vineyard: 30 ha of vines averaging 25 years of age, on slopes on the right bank of the Dordogne. Vines planted are Merlot (60%), Cabernet Franc (20%), Malbec (10%), and Cabernet Sauvignon (10%) for the reds and Sauvignon (50%), Sémillon (25%) and Muscadelle (25%) for the whites.
Terroir: Boulbène which is a type of sandy-clay silt and Périgord sand.
Viticulture: Traditional, with grassing down between rows, mechanical pruning, leaf-plucking and green harvesting. Philippe and Thierry follow the principles of "la lutte raisonnée", only spraying when and where necessary.
Vinification: Traditional for the Bergerac Rouge. Maceration on the skins and fermentation at low temperature for the dry whites and rosé. The Montravel Sec is vinified in barriques and the Côtes de Bergerac Rouge is matured in oak.
Visits: Open every day from 9.00 a.m. to 12.00 a.m. and 2.00 p.m. to 6.00 p.m. Visit of the winery by appointment. French, English and Spanish are spoken.
History: Château de la Mallevieille is an eighteenth century manor house and was formerly a staging post between Sainte-Foy-la-Grande and the Périgord. It was mentioned in Féret's work of 1903 and the property has been owned by Philippe and Hélène Biau since 1983. In 1997 they were joined by Nadia and Thierry Bernardinis with their 7 hectares of Montravel near Fougueyrolles to form Vignobles Biau.
The Wines: Bergerac Sec and Rosé
   Bergerac Rouge
   Montravel Sec
   Côtes de Bergerac Rouge
   Côtes de Bergerac Moelleux
Comments: The wines have been regular award winners and are exported throughout Europe and to Australia. The Bergerac Sec is a great introduction to the range: pale lemon in colour with a tinge of green, a nose of cut grass and Sauvignon again dominant on the palate with fresh gooseberry flavours and nice balanced acidity. We enjoyed all the reds, from the 2005 Bergerac, bursting with fruits of the forest but with a bit of grip on the finish; the 2001 Côtes had spicy dark fruit aromas with soft tannins on the finish; star however was the flagship "Imagine" Côtes de Bergerac with warm spicy cinnamon nose, great depth of black fruit flavours, powerful and rounded with a long, long finish.
In the U.K.: Coyne Vintners Ltd., tel: 0151 928 3833

Château Masburel

Owner/Winemaker: Julian Robbins
Address: Fougueyrolles, 33220
Ste-Foy-la-Grande
Tel: (0)5 53 24 77 73
Fax: (0)5 53 24 27 30
Email: chateau-masburel@wanadoo.fr
How to get there: Take the D708 out of Port
Ste Foy, direction Montpon and Château
Masburel is signposted on the left after
about 2 km, on the "Route des Vins".

Appellations: Montravel, Haut Montravel; Côtes de Bergerac, Bergerac.
Price: Band C
Vineyard: 23 ha planted with Cabernet Sauvignon, Merlot, Cabernet Franc, Malbec and for the whites, Sauvignon, Sémillon and Muscadelle. Vines are up to 55 years old.
Terroir: South-facing slopes on a mixture of clay, chalk, limestone and sand.
Viticulture: Olivia Donnan followed the "lutte raisonnée" philosophy with minimal use of chemicals and was moving towards an increasingly organic approach. New plantings have been at exceptionally high densities ranging from 8000 to 13000 vines per hectare which is well above the legal AOC requirement.
Vinification: Grapes are picked very ripe at very low yields of 20-30 hl/ha. Lady Masburel white is vinified in concrete vats, Château Masburel in French oak. Both are lees stirred for one year. All reds are fermented in concrete vats with malolactic fermentation taking place in French oak. Long maceration of 6-8 weeks. Fermentation is fully temperature-controlled. Wines are aged mainly in French oak, of which one third is new, and the barrel store is climate-controlled. Four or five different coopers are used depending on the grape variety.
Visits: Full tour of the chai and vineyard is possible. Château Masburel was winner of the "Prix d'Aquitaine" in 2003 for Wine Tourism awarded by the Chamber of Commerce and Industry in Bordeaux. Monday to Friday, 9.00 a.m. to 12.00 a.m. and 2.00 p.m. to 6.00 p.m. Weekends by arrangement. English and French spoken.
History: Founded in 1740 by Jean de Sembellie, consul to King Louis XV of France, Château Masburel has been producing wine for nearly 270 years. The property was bought in 1997 by English couple Neil and Olivia Donnan and following substantial investment in the winery and the vineyard, the wines have gained a reputation as some of the best in the region. The property has recently been sold to Julian Robbins.
The Wines: Montravel - Mon Ravel Boléro (red)
Château Masburel (white)
Côtes de Bergerac - Château Masburel (red)
Lady Masburel (red)
Haut-Montravel - Château Masburel moelleux
Comments: High density planting and low yields are key factors here. The wines have a structure and complexity that show that Bergerac wines deserve to be taken seriously. Flagship wine is the Boléro, dark and dense, a complex nose of prunes and chocolate, dark fruit flavours and ripe tannins...but the rest are good too.
In the U.K.:   Fine Claret Sellers, tel: 07980 290505
Waitrose

Château Masmontet

Owner/Winemaker: Thibaut Guillermier

Address: 24230 Vélines

Tel: (0)5 53 74 39 56

Fax: (0)5 53 74 39 60

How to get there: Vélines is just off the D936 between Castillon and Ste-Foy-la-Grande. From Vélines take the road to Nastringues and follow the signs.

Appellations: Bergerac, Côtes de Bergerac, Montravel, Côtes de Montravel

Price: A/B

Vineyard: 22 ha of which just over half is devoted to white wine production. Vines are on average 25 years old but certain parcels have vines over 90 years old. Vines planted are Merlot (40%), Malbec (25%), Cabernet Franc (20%) and Cabernet Sauvignon (15%) and for the whites, Sauvignon (50%), Sémillon (25%), Muscadelle (20%) and Ugni Blanc (5%).

Terroir: Mainly clay and limestone with 20% being siliceous clay soils.

Viticulture: Worked according to "la lutte raisonnée" since 2001 with manual and mechanical pruning and harvesting, green harvesting on part of the vineyard, mechanical leaf plucking on 80% of the property. Trained in the single and double Guyot systems, vines are planted at 2500, 3300 and most recently 5000 to the hectare. The rows are grassed down either in totality or every other row, depending on the weather each year.

Vinification: Grapes are normally de-stemmed except for the sweet wines. Vinification is specific to each wine but by and large involves long maceration for the reds, maceration on the skins for the whites for one to three days, followed by cool fermentation. Wines are matured for 5 to 18 months in oak of which 15% is new. Of particular interest is the use of demi-muids made of acacia for the white Côtes de Montravel and Haut-Montravel.

Visits: Monday to Friday 8.00 a.m. to 12.00 a.m. and 2.00 p.m. to 6.30 p.m. Weekend by appointment. French and English spoken.

History: Thibaut is a third generation winemaker, having taken over from his father in 2001, the family having bought the property in 1967. The property belonged to a Monsieur de Masmontet, Chevalier du Roi under Napoleon.

The Wines: Montravel Rouge "M de M"
     Montravel Sec
     Côtes de Montravel liquoreux

Comments: When I called to see Thibaut he had just received a consignment of new acacia barrels. Do try the Côtes de Montravel which is vinified and aged in acacia and which has a pronounced nose of resin and pears, the pears carrying through to the lightish palate with tinned peaches that is more moelleux than liquoreux. The wine is unfined and unfiltered and will probably have thrown a deposit. What stood out here, however, was the "M de M" Montravel with warm clove spices on the nose and flavours of rich dark fruits, ripe and mellow, with well-integrated tannins.

In the U.K.: Not available.

Château Michel de Montaigne

Owner/Winemaker: Christian Mähler-Besse
Address: 24230 St Michel de Montaigne
Tel: (0)5 53 58 63 93
Fax: (0)5 53 58 63 93
How to get there: From the D936 just east of Castillon, take the D21 north towards Montpon and after about 4 km look out for the signs to the château on the right.
Appellations: Bergerac, Côtes de Bergerac; Côtes de Montravel
Price: Band A
Vineyard: 20 hectares of which 17 are devoted to reds and 3 to whites. Planting for the reds is Merlot (40%), Cabernet Franc (40%) and Cabernet Sauvignon (20%) and for the whites, Sauvignon (95%) and Sémillon (5%).

Terroir: As a continuation of the Côtes de Castillon, the soils are clay-limestone, Fronsadais molasse over Castillon limestone.

Viticulture: Planting density is 5000 vines to the hectare and most are trained on the double Guyot system. There is a metre of grass between rows and organic fertilisers are used every other year. Leaf thinning takes place over half the vineyard with green harvesting as necessary for the Essais cuvée. There is a "lutte raisonnée" approach to spraying, yields are 50 to 55 hl/ha and harvesting is by machine.

Vinification: Grapes are de-stemmed and crushed before being fermented in a variety of tanks - stainless steel, cement and glass fibre. Cuvaison lasts from 15 to 30 days depending on the wine and the Essais is matured in oak for 12 months.

Visits: In July and August, open every day from 10.00 a.m. to 6.30 p.m. In May, June, September and October, 10.00 a.m. to 12.00 a.m. and 2.00 p.m. to 6.30 p.m., closed Monday and Tuesday. In February to April, November and December, 10.00 a.m. to 12.00 a.m. and 2.00 p.m. to 5.30 p.m., closed Monday and Tuesday. Closed in January. The winery and vineyard can not be visited but you can combine a wine tasting with a visit to Montaigne's tower.

History: The famous philosopher and mayor of Bordeaux Michel Eyquem de Montaigne was born and died in the château where he wrote his "Essais" between 1571 and 1592. From his tower he could see the vineyards of Montravel and he was a great believer in the benefits of drinking in moderation but condemned excesses: "No opportunity to drink should be refused, but rather always keep this desire in mind" (Essais II,2) The tower where he wrote in his library fortunately escaped the fire of 1885. There are guided tours of the 14th century tower.

The Wines: Bergerac Rouge
Bergerac Rouge Les Essais

Comments: We tasted the 2003 Bergerac which was taking on brick red tones and had a pleasant nose of spice and fruit cake. On the palate there was plenty of fruit, it was rich and smooth with a pleasingly dry finish. Les Essais 2001 was a deep dark red, just beginning to turn at the rim and had a wonderful cedary, cigar-box nose, with great depth of spicy red fruits, a touch of liquorice, and soft well-integrated oak tannins.

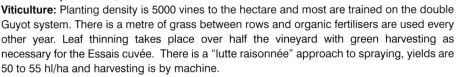

In the U.K.: Not available.

Château Moulin Caresse

Owner/Winemaker: Sylvie & Jean-François Deffarge
Address: Couin, 24230 St Antoine de Breuilh
Tel: (0)5 53 27 55 58
Fax: (0)5 53 27 07 39
Email: moulin.caresse@cegetel.net
How to get there: At St Antoine de Breuilh just west of Ste Foy on the D936, turn to the north opposite the chemist's and follow signs for the domain from that point.
Appellations: Bergerac Rouge, Rosé, Côtes de Bergerac Rouge; Montravel Rouge, Sec, Haut Montravel
Price: Band B
Vineyard: The 28 hectares are planted with Merlot, Cabernet Sauvignon, Cabernet Franc and Malbec and for the whites, Sauvignon Blanc, Sauvignon Gris, Sémillon and Muscadelle. The vines are about 30 years old.
Terroir: South and south-west facing, the slopes are clay-limestone and the plateau boulbène, on an iron-rich clay base with limestone containing flint and fossilized oysters, a terroir which brings typical minerality to the Montravel appellation.
Viticulture: The whole vineyard is being converted to a density of 5500 vines to the hectare, trained high on the single Guyot system. Leaves are trimmed around the fruit to promote healthy ripening with green harvesting for low yields. The soil is hoed beneath the vines rather than use herbicides and grassed down between rows.
Vinification: The winery is equipped with the latest efficient equipment. The grapes are sorted by hand with maceration under inert gas for the whites before temperature-controlled fermentation and maturation on the lees in barrel. The reds undergo micro-oxygenation on the marc and spend up to 18 months in French oak. The winery meets European standards for the treatment of waste water and protection of the environment. The reception area offers fine views over the valley.
Visits: Monday to Friday 9.00 a.m. to 12.00 a.m. and 2.00 p.m. to 6.00 p.m. Weekends by appointment. French and English spoken.
History: A family property dating from the eighteenth century, Jean-François' grandfather Paul co-founded the co-operative at Port Ste Foy in 1935. Jean-François took over in 1980 and terminated his contract with the co-op in 1993, having created a winery and completely restructured the vineyard which has grown from 12 hectares in 1980 to its present 28 hectares.
The Wines: Montravel Sauvignon
                 Montravel rouge Cent pour 100
Comments: The whole place oozes class and the Deffarges are really professional in their approach. The Montravel Sauvignon, which actually contains 30% Sauvignon Gris and 10% Sémillon, was bright lemon in colour with a fresh citrus and slightly biscuity nose, and again citrus flavours on the palate, most refreshing balance but with good weight in the mouth. The red Montravel Cent pour 100 was a great advert for the appellation. Deep and dense in colour, with a toasty coffee nose and rich plum and damson fruit wrapped in teeth-coating tannins that promised several years of improvement to come.

In the U.K.:   Winegrowers Direct Ltd, tel: 01954-230176

Château Moulin-Garreau

Owner/Winemaker: Alain & Nathalie Péronnet

Address: Garreau, 24230 Lamothe-Montravel
Tel: (0)5 53 61 26 97/ (0)6 80 21 28 68
Fax: (0)5 53 61 26 97
Email: aperonnet@wanadoo.fr

How to get there: At Lamothe-Montravel on the D936, turn off on the D9 towards Saint-Michel-de-Montaigne, taking a right turn before the village, and Moulin-Garreau is on the right.

Appellations: Bergerac, Côtes de Bergerac, Montravel

Price: Band B

Vineyard: 13 ha of vines, south-facing, which are on average 30 years old. Grape varieties here are restricted to Merlot and Cabernet Sauvignon for the reds, Sauvignon and Sémillon for the whites.

Terroir: On the plateau of St-Michel-de-Montaigne, sandy clay soils on Castillon limestone with fossilised oysters and some iron and manganese deposits. On the slopes, siliceous limestone and clay soils on Fronsadais molasse.

Viticulture: Principles of "lutte raisonnée" are followed, moving towards an organic approach. Any fertilisers used are natural, such as compost and guano. Half the vines are planted at 3500 to the hectare for traditional Bergerac, and at 5000 and 6200 for the Montravel and top Bergeracs. Rows are alternately ploughed or grassed down, leaf thinning is done by hand with green harvesting in July and August. Yields are kept at 35 hl/ha for the whites and 45 hl/ha for the reds.

Vinification: Pre-fermentation maceration, followed by temperature-controlled fermentation in concrete vats. The dry white matures on the lees with the Miss Diane cuvée spending 12 months in oak, and the red equivalent up to 18 months in Allier oak, one third renewed each year. Micro-oxygenation is sometimes used during fermentation to increase yeast colonies and afterwards it can be used instead of racking to correct any reductive flavours.

Visits: Every day, 10.00 a.m. to 12.00 a.m. and 1.30 p.m. to 5.30 p.m. Advisable to ring beforehand. French and English spoken.

History: Formerly known as "Moulin de Garreau" and in the 1903 edition of the Féret "Bergerac et ses Vins" simply as "Garreau", the property was bought in December 2004 by Alain and Nathalie Péronnet, who were returning to their agricultural roots having been pharmacist and company secretary respectively in Paris.

The Wines: Bergerac Rouge Honneur à Jeanne
Montravel Sec Les Régates
Montravel Rouge Miss Diane

Comments: Best of the wines tasted was Les Régates which is half and half Sauvignon Sémillon with a honeyed citrussy nose, a hint of grapefruit in the mouth, full rounded flavours, almost creamy and with a long finish.

In the U.K.: Not available.

Château Pique-Sègue

Owner/Winemaker: Philip & Marianne Mallard

Address: 33220 Port Ste Foy

Tel: (0)5 53 58 52 52

Fax: (0)5 53 58 77 01

Email: Marianne.mallard@wanadoo.fr

How to get there: From St Méard-de-Gurçon take the Le Fleix road, the D32, towards Ponchapt and follow the signs to the domain.

Appellations: Bergerac; Montravel, Côtes de Montravel, Haut-Montravel

Price: Band A/B

Vineyard: Quite a large property of 88 hectares, situated on the Libourne promontory at 150 metres above sea level, planted with Merlot, Cabernet Sauvignon and Cabernet Franc, Sémillon, Sauvignon and Muscadelle. Vines on average are 20 years old.

Terroir: Clay and chalk on Agenais molasse.

Viticulture: The Mallards adopt a "lutte raisonnée" approach which means the use of chemical weed-killers and fertilisers has been reduced in favour of organic products and more labour-intensive methods. There is also a meteorological monitoring centre on site. Harvesting is manual and mechanical, depending on the wine being made.

Vinification: The winery is very modern and equipped to a very high technical specification. There is temperature control of fermentation of both reds and whites, two pneumatic presses and refrigerated tartrate precipitation tanks. Micro-oxygenation is also used to avoid over-handling the wine and to make for gentler extraction. The Bergerac Rouge is matured in vats or oak barrels for 12 to 15 months. The dry white is kept on its fine lees for 6 to 12 months.

Visits: Monday to Friday, from 9.00 a.m. to 12.00 a.m. and 2.00 p.m. to 5.00 p.m. French and English spoken.

History: Classified in the fourteenth century by the Archbishop of Bordeaux, the vineyard was described at the end of the 19th century as "one of the most beautifully sited in the region". It was acquired by Englishman Philip Mallard, who hails from Staffordshire (as do his bull terriers) and his French wife Marianne in 1990 and they have developed the winery which includes a laboratory. They also have a herd of pedigree Limousin cattle and a champion French bull which contribute to the organic fertiliser!

The Wines: Montravel Sec
                   Bergerac Rouge, Rosé
                   Côtes de Montravel
                   Montravel Rouge Anima Vitis

Wines are also produced under the Château Dauzan La Vergne label.

Comments: The Montravel white had a hugely honeyed nose followed by fresh green plum acidity with good balance. The red Anima Vitis we tasted was from 2002 and had a complex nose of tobacco, cedar and smoke with just a whiff of the farmyard. It had medium weight in the mouth with soft fruit and mellow tannins.

In the U.K.: Not available.

Château Puy-Servain

Owner: SCEA Puy-Servain
Winemaker: Daniel Hecquet
Address: 33220 Port Ste Foy et Ponchapt
Tel: (0)5 53 24 77 27
Fax: (0)5 53 58 37 43
Email: oenovit.puyservain@wanadoo.fr
How to get there: The domain is clearly signposted from St Méard-de-Gurçon, Le Fleix and Port Ste Foy.

Appellations: Bergerac Rouge, Rosé; Montravel, Haut-Montravel
Price: Band B
Vineyard: 50 hectares planted with Cabernet Franc (20%), Cabernet Sauvignon (10%) and Merlot (70%) for the reds, Sauvignon Blanc and Gris (45%), Sémillon (50%) and Muscadelle (5%) for the whites. The vines average 25 years of age, half white, half red.
Terroir: Situated at the highest point of the slopes of Montravel, overlooking the Dordogne, on varied clay-limestone soils which contain a surprising amount of flint.
Viticulture: A "lutte raisonnée" approach is adopted with organic fertilisers being used when necessary and pesticides kept to a minimum. Single Guyot system of training with short pruning. Vines are planted at up to 7500 to the hectare for the Merlot. Every other row is ploughed or grassed down. Leaf thinning on both sides is done by hand in August/September for the sweet wines and by machine for the rest on the east side only as required. Yields are 40-50 hl/ha and just 25 hl/ha for the Haut-Montravel.
Vinification: A modern winery and underground barrel cellar have been built recently. The best cuvées undergo fermentation and maturation in oak barrels and the Haut-Montravel is made from noble rot affected Sémillon using cryoextraction techniques.
Visits: Monday to Friday, 8.00 a.m. to 12.00 a.m. and 2.00 p.m. to 6.00 p.m. Weekends by arrangement. French and English spoken.
History: Puy-Servain has been in the Hecquet family for three generations. Daniel Hecquet is also a well-respected consultant oenologist, one-time head of the CIVRB laboratory with responsibility for sweet wines having worked in Bordeaux and specifically at Château d'Yquem. Along with Serge Dubard of Château Laulerie, he was instrumental in getting recognition for the Montravel Rouge appellation, dependent on a planting density of 5000 vines to the hectare and acceptance only after tasting post-bottling which is rare amongst French appellations. Wines are also sold under the Château Calabre (Bergerac and Montravel) and Domaine des Bertranoux (Pécharmant) labels.
The Wines: Terrement Haut-Montravel
              Montravel Rouge Vieilles Vignes
Comments: The wines tasted were out of the top drawer. The red Montravel Vieilles Vignes 2003 had gentle oak vanillas on the nose, was deep and dense in colour, almost opaque, with spicy dark berry fruits, soft and rounded with a hint of dryness on the finish. The Haut-Montravel 2003 was a fabulous liquoreux by any standards. Heady aromas of honeyed pink grapefruit and pineapple gave way to a palate of intense candied fruits but it was clean and fresh tasting too.
In the U.K.:   Laytons, tel: 020 7288 8888, Milton Sandford, tel: 01628 829449
              i Vintners, tel: 020 8948 0010

Château le Raz

Owner: GAEC du Maine
Winemaker: Barde family
Address: 24610 St Méard de Gurçon
Tel: 9)05 53 82 48 41
Fax: (0)5 53 80 07 47
Email: vignobles-barde@le-raz.com
How to get there: Just off the D708 between Port Ste Foy and Montpon, south-west of St Méard-de-Gurçon.
Appellations: Bergerac Rouge, Sec, Rosé; Montravel, Côtes de Montravel, Haut-Montravel
Price: Band A/B
Vineyard: 60 ha of vines comprising Merlot, Cabernet Sauvignon, Malbec and Cabernet Franc, Sauvignon, Sémillon and Muscadelle. Vines for the whites are 15 to 45 years old, and for the reds 20 to 30 years old.
Terroir: Soils are clay-limestone with poor sandy-clay boulbène, south-facing.
Viticulture: The vineyard is grassed down between rows. Practices include hard pruning, de-budding in May, with manual canopy management, and a "lutte raisonnée" approach to spraying. The harvest takes place when the grapes are almost over-ripe. A third of the vineyard has currently been replanted at 6000 vines to the hectare for the Montravel.
Vinification: The dry whites are macerated on the skins, cold settled and matured on the lees. The reds have regular pigeage during fermentation and Patrick Barde was one of the first to use the technique of micro-oxygenation in the area. Maturation takes place in both tank and oak barrels, top quality oak being sourced in the Dordogne.
Visits: Monday to Friday, from 9.00 a.m. to 12.30 p.m. and 2.30 p.m. to 6.30 p.m. Saturday by appointment. French spoken.
History: Château le Raz is a fine country house dating back to the seventeenth century. Its roofs are topped by weather-vanes in the form of fleur-de-lys which escaped the ravages of the Revolution. The winemaking Barde family can be traced back to 1610 in the commune. In 1967 the Barde brothers, Patrick, Cyril, Régis and Gil, formed a GAEC (Groupement Agricole d'Exploitation en Commun) as the property gradually expanded. Today, over 70% of production is exported.
The Wines: Montravel Sec Cuvée Grand Chêne
Montravel Rouge "Les Filles"
Haut-Montravel Cuvée Pierres Blanches liquoreux
Comments: The Montravel Rouge Les Filles had aromas of burnt toast, tar and a whiff of the farmyard, rounded flavours of black fruits and pleasantly soft tannins. The Montravel Sec Cuvée Grand Chêne seemed to offer a perfect balance between the freshness of the Sauvignon and the complexity afforded by careful oak maturation. The unoaked version was good too with a crisp Sauvignon nose followed by soft fruitiness backed by clean acidity.

In the U.K.:   AC Wines Ltd., tel: 020 86955959, Elixir Fine Wines, tel: 020 87681346
Trout Wines 01264 781472, Four Vintners, tel: 020 77397335
Hill Drinks, tel: 01268 792611 & Sommelier's Choice, tel: 020 86899643

Château la Ressaudie

Owner/Winemaker: Jean and Evelyne Rebeyrolle

Address: 33220 Port Ste Foy
Tel: (0)5 53 24 71 48
Fax: (0)5 53 58 52 29
Email: vinleressaudie@hotmail.fr

How to get there: Take the Montpon road out of Port Ste Foy and after 1 km, at the top of the hill, look out for a sign to the domain on the right.

Appellations: Bergerac, Montravel

Price: Band A/B

Vineyard: 23 hectares, the majority planted with red grape varieties, namely Merlot (60%), Cabernet Sauvignon (20%) and Cabernet Franc (20%). For the whites, two thirds of the area is planted with Sauvignon and the rest with Sémillon. The vines are 10 to 15 years old.

Terroir: Situated on the hills above Port Ste Foy on the right bank of the Dordogne, clay and sandy soils over limestone.

Viticulture: The Rebeyrolles subscribe to the "lutte raisonnée" approach with little use of insecticides. At the moment, the vineyard is totally grassed down but they will be going back to ploughing every other row. New plantings are at 5000 vines to the hectare in line with the red Montravel appellation and about one third has so far been replanted. Leaf thinning is done by hand for the Montravel Rouge and rigorous pruning is practised instead of green harvesting.

Vinification: The chai dates from 1900 with epoxy-lined cement vats and some stainless steel and fibre glass. The top cuvées are aged in oak barriques, mainly French with some American, and usually one or two years old.

Visits: Every day from 9.00 a.m. to 12.00 a.m. and 3.00 p.m. to 7.00 p.m. It is best to ring first. French, English, Italian and a little German spoken.

History: The property has been in the family for six generations and featured in the Féret guide of 1903. Jean has been at the helm since 1981 and the country house also offers chambres d'hôte and gîte with swimming pool.

The Wines: Bergerac Rouge
Bergerac Rouge Rive Droite
Montravel Rouge
Haut-Montravel

Comments: The Bergerac Rouge was great value with its rich plummy flavours, a touch of spice and soft tannins. The Rive Droite 2003 was still bright and youthful with rich spicy oak vanillas on the nose and soft almost sweet fruit in the mouth with a hint of liquorice and figs, silky and seductive.

In the U.K.:   Maison Liedberg, tel: 01923 710479

Union Vinicole Bergerac-Le Fleix

Owner/Winemaker: 176 members of the co-operative.
Address: 24130 Le Fleix and 70, bd. Santraille, 24100 Bergerac
Tel: (0)5 53 24 64 32
Fax: (0)5 53 57 16 27
How to get there: The Le Fleix shop is in the centre of the village, follow the signs. The Bergerac shop is near the railway station and is signposted.
Appellations: Bergerac, Pécharmant, Monbazillac, Montravel
Price: Band B
Vineyard: 1300 hectares of AOC vineyard planted with the usual varieties.
Terroir: The considerable area of vines is planted on a whole range of Périgourdin soils including sand and gravel, clay-limestone and boulbène.
Viticulture: The Union works hard to respect the environment whilst producing healthy grapes and the "lutte raisonnée" approach has been backed by Agri-Confiance certification since 2005. Various contracts are in place between the cave and the growers depending on the level of wine produced - top cuvées, AOC or vin de pays. Growers can elect to have the co-operative vinify and mature their wines and commercialise them themselves, or more commonly, to simply sell their grapes to the cave and be paid depending on the weight and a number of factors such as fruit quality, grape variety, degree of alcohol and selling price of the wine produced.
Vinification: State-of-the-art equipment is in place with a total tank capacity of 150,000 hectolitres which allows some domain wines to be vinified separately. There is some oak maturation at Bergerac with the best wines spending 12 months in barriques. There are over 1000 barrels at the Cave de Bergerac which makes it the largest barrel store in the region.
Visits: In summer, Tuesday to Saturday, 8.30 a.m. to 12.30 p.m. and 2.00 p.m. to 7.00 p.m. In winter, 8.30 a.m. to 12.30 p.m. and 2.00 p.m. to 6.00 p.m., closing at 12.30 p.m. on Saturdays (Bergerac only). Mondays 2.00 p.m. to 7.00 p.m. in summer. French, English and Spanish spoken. The winery at Bergerac can be visited.
History: The co-operative at Le Fleix was founded in 1940 and the Bergerac co-op in 1951, the two merging in 1990. The Union Vinicole advises its members on choice of vine, planting and all work in the vineyard in order to ensure the best quality fruit.
The Wines: Pécharmant Vieux Sapin
Monbazillac Domaine de Leyrissat
Montravel Rouge Ch. Roche de Castérie
Bergerac Domaine de la Vaure
Comments: The Roche de Castérie was well-balanced with soft velvety fruit, an oak dominated nose and well-integrated tannins. The Vieux Sapin was also very good with soft discreet tannins, fresh blackcurrant fruit and well-integrated oak. The Domaine de la Vaure has long been a favourite of mine and is great value and the Monbazillac had medium weight with orange zest on the nose and the palate, flavours too of peaches and candied fruits.

In the U.K: Not available.

Eymet-Issigeac-Lalinde

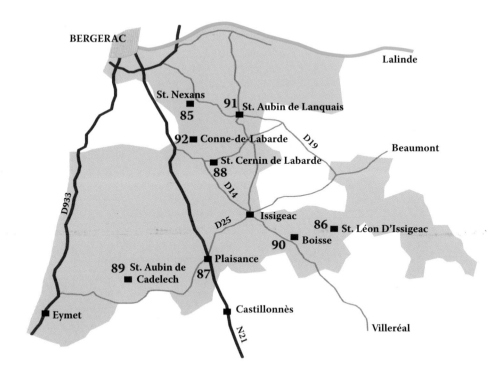

BERGERAC

Lalinde

St. Nexans
91 St. Aubin de Lanquais
85

92 Conne-de-Labarde
Beaumont
D19

St. Cernin de Labarde
88
D14

D25
Issigeac
86 St. Léon D'Issigeac
90 Boisse

89 St. Aubin de
Cadelech
87
Plaisance

Eymet

Castillonnès

Villeréal

D933
N21

85.
*Domaine du
Bois de Pourquié*

86.
*Le Clos du
Breil*

87.
*Clos du Pech
Bessou*

88.
*Château les
Saintongers
d'Hautefeuille*

89.
*Domaine du
Siorac*

90.
*Château Tertres
du Plantou*

91.
*Château Tour
de Grangemont*

92.
*Vignoble des
Verdots*

Domaine du Bois de Pourquié

Owner/Winemaker: Marlène and Alain Mayet

Address: Le Bois de Pourquié, 24560
Conne-de-Labarde

Tel: (0)5 53 58 25 58

Fax: (0)5 53 61 34 59

Email: domaine-du-bois-de-pourquie@wanadoo.fr

How to get there: Take the N21 Agen road out of
Bergerac and after about 8 km turn left towards St
Nexans then right towards Conne-de-Labarde and
the property is on the left.

Appellations: Bergerac, Côtes de Bergerac,
Monbazillac

Price: Band B

Vineyard: 30 ha of which 17 are planted with red varieties, mainly Merlot with the Cabernets,
and 13 with white, mainly Sémillon with Sauvignon Blanc and Gris, the vines being aged 25
to 30 years.

Terroir: There is a diversity of terroirs on two sites: siliceous clay, boulbène and limestone.

Viticulture: General grassing down between rows. The vineyard is currently being replanted
at 5000 vines to the hectare, 8 hectares having been completed by the end of 2007. Yields
are as low as 15 to 20 hl/ha for the Monbazillac.

Vinification: Whites are macerated on the skins with the rosé being made by the saignée
method. Maceration time for the reds depends on the style of wine being made. Dry whites
and rosé spend some time on the lees whilst the Côtes de Bergerac is matured in new and
one-year-old oak barriques.

Visits: Every day except Sunday from 9.00 a.m. to 7.00 p.m. for tastings. By arrangement for
visit of the winery. French spoken.

History: The Mayets go back to the 16th century when they were cathedral builders. In
about 1830 they settled in the area between the hill of Monbazillac and the Dordogne river
and the domain dates from 1852 when it was a farm with very few vines. It was only after the
Second World War that the vineyard really started to grow and in 1971 the first bottle was sold
commercially. Alain started to help his father in 1979, forming a GAEC with him in 1983. Alain
and his wife hope that one of their sons will soon join them to maintain 150 years of family
winemaking tradition.

The Wines: Révélation Rouge
    Révélation Blanc sec

Comments: We did not taste the flagship Révélation range but the 2003 Côtes de Bergerac
was probably at its best with aromas of violets and deep almost port-like flavours. The 2006
Rosé has won a string of awards.

In the U.K.: Not available.

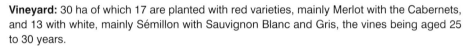

Le Clos du Breil

Owner/Winemaker: Jean Vergniaud

Address: Le Breil, 24560 St Léon d'Issigeac

Tel: (0)5 53 58 75 55

Fax: (0)5 53 58 75 55

Email: leclosdubreil@free.fr

How to get there: From Issigeac, south-east of Bergerac, take the D14 towards Villeréal and just after leaving town, turn left on the D23 to St Léon.

Appellations: Bergerac, Côtes de Bergerac

Price: Band A/B

Vineyard: Just 8 hectares planted mainly with red varieties comprising Merlot (60%), Cabernet Sauvignon (28%) and Cabernet Franc (12%). The whites are recent plantings of Sémillon (50%), Sauvignon (33%) and Muscadelle (17%). The red varieties are 25 years old.

Terroir: Clay-limestone and deep clays.

Viticulture: 80% of the work is done by hand. The rows are grassed down except for the young vines which are ploughed. Spraying is not systematic and leaf thinning and green harvesting are practised as necessary. Harvesting is by machine except for the white varieties and the younger vines.

Vinification: Traditional vinification in tank with varieties and parcels being treated separately. Cool maceration before fermentation which is temperature-controlled. Eight to ten months maturation in tank for the majority with the Côtes de Bergerac spending some time in oak.

Visits: Monday to Saturday from 9.00 a.m. to 7.00 p.m. French and English spoken.

History: A family holding since the 19th century, specialising in the production of wine since 1994.

The Wines: Côtes de Bergerac Rouge
Bergerac Rouge Cuvée l'Odyssée

Comments: We tasted the 2002 Bergerac Rouge which had retained a bright freshness of colour and the taste was all brambles and damsons with a hint of spice and chocolate. The 2005 Odyssée showed a touch more complexity with quite a floral nose and spicy rich berry flavours with tannins that were still quite pronounced.

In the U.K.: Not available.

Clos du Pech Bessou

Owner/Winemaker: Pascal and Sylvie Thomassin

Address: La Pouge, 24560 Plaisance

Tel: (0)5 53 24 53 00/ (0)6 85 63 23 93

Fax: (0)5 53 61 76 79

Email: closdupechbessou@wanadoo.fr

How to get there: Plaisance is 20 km south of Bergerac on the N21. Continue through Plaisance towards Castillonnès and after about 800m, at the top of the hill, turn right then right again after a further 500m.

Appellations: Bergerac Sec, Rouge, Rosé, Côtes de Bergerac Moelleux

Price: Band A

Vineyard: Just 7 hectares planted mainly with red varieties: Merlot (40%), Cabernet Franc (40%) and Malbec (20%). For the moelleux, Sémillon (70%) and Muscadelle (30%). The red vines are about 20 years old, the white varieties recent plantings now 5 years old.

Terroir: Clay-limestone soils.

Viticulture: Most vines are planted at 3000 to the hectare with more recent plantings at 4000. There is some grassing down especially on the slopes to help prevent erosion. Spraying is done only when necessary and there is some leaf thinning though it is not systematic. Harvesting is by machine except for the moelleux. Yields average 50 hl/ha.

Vinification: There is some maceration on the skins depending on the wine and temperature of the fermentation is strictly controlled especially for the white and rosé in order to preserve the aromas. Maturation takes place in tank apart from the Merrain which is aged in oak barrels, half of which are new.

Visits: Monday to Saturday, 9.00 a.m. to 12.30 p.m. and 2.00 p.m. to 6.00 p.m. French and English spoken.

History: A family property taken over by brother and sister Pascal and Sylvie Thomassin, the farm comprised just two and a half hectares of vines in 2000 and this has now grown to its present 7 hectares. With Sylvie's arrival in 2000, the property started to sell directly from the chai and at wine fairs.

The Wines: Bergerac Rosé
Le Merrain de Pech Bessou

Comments: We preferred the reds here. The Bergerac 2004 was deep in colour with hints of tar and soft leather on the nose and firm blackcurrant fruit and tannins with a pleasantly dry finish. The 2002 oaked version had a smoky nose with tar in evidence again, soft rounded dark fruits, well-integrated tannins that had left no hard edges.

In the U.K.: Not available.

Château les Saintongers d'Hautefeuille

Owner/Winemaker: Catherine d'Hautefeuille

Address: Les Saintongers, 24560 Saint Cernin de Labarde

Tel: (0)5 53 24 32 84

Fax: (0)5 53 57 77 18

Email: adhautefeuille@hotmail.fr

How to get there: Take the N21 Agen road from Bergerac and after 10 km take the D14 towards Issigeac. After about 4 km look out for a small road on the left signposted "La Barde, Les Saintongers". Pass an old château on the right and the domain is on the right up a rough track.

Price: Band B

Appellations: Côtes de Bergerac

Vineyard: A tiny holding of just 2.5 hectares planted half and half with Merlot and Cabernet Sauvignon. The vines are eight years old.

Terroir: Clay-limestone soils on a rocky subsoil on the Issigeac plateau.

Viticulture: The d'Hautefeuille family subscribes to the "lutte raisonnée" movement with meetings each week to share ideas and keep informed of any potential problems. Grassing down between rows effectively covers about 40% of the surface. Half the buds are removed in March with green harvesting later if necessary. High density planting at 5500 vines to the hectare.

Vinification: Stainless steel tanks are used for both alcoholic and malolactic fermentations with yields kept at 40 hl/ha., which equates to one bottle of wine per vine. The wine spends 12 to 16 months in barrique, the oak sourced in central France. As with Montravel Rouge, Côtes de Bergerac Rouge is only accredited with AOC status after it has been bottled.

Visits: Monday to Saturday. Please ring beforehand.

History: Catherine is the qualified winemaker and husband Vianney comes from a background of cereal farming in Picardy. They started at les Saintongers some ten years ago although quality wine has been produced here since the beginning of the last century. 2001 was their first vintage and numerous gold medals have followed.

The Wines: Just the one: Côtes de Bergerac Rouge

Comments: The name of the property is quite a mouthful and the same could be said of the wine. There is only one wine produced here but it is worth making the detour. The style is rather different with more emphasis on Cabernet Sauvignon. The 2003 had an attractive nose of blueberries and prunes, liquorice and vanilla, and in the mouth fruit and oak in perfect harmony and a long finish of soft tannins with a hint of figs. Minimum purchase is six bottles.

In the U.K.: Not available.

Domaine du Siorac

Owner/Winemaker: Jean-Paul Landat

Address: 24500 St Aubin de Cadelech

Tel: (0)5 53 74 52 90

Fax: (0)5 53 58 35 32

Email: j-paul@domainedusiorac.fr

How to get there: Best reached from the D25 Eymet to Castillonnès road. Look out for the signs.

Appellations: Bergerac Rouge, Sec, Rosé; Côtes de Bergerac

Price: Band A

Vineyard: 23 ha planted with vines of an average age of 23 years for the reds and 17 years for the whites. Varieties planted are Merlot (40%), Cabernet Sauvignon (30%) and Cabernet Franc (30%) for the reds, Sémillon (55%), Muscadelle (5%) and Sauvignon (40% of which 15% is Gris).

Terroir: Clay-limestone soils on three different sites including the plateau at St Capraise on Monbazillac limestone which is managed for friend, Englishman George Vellacott, and sold under the Château Casse Bessou label.

Viticulture: Rows between the vines are alternately ploughed or grassed down. Leaf trimming takes place on the easterly or northerly side. This property is quite unique in producing "verjus", the juice of under-ripe grapes which is used in cooking, most of the production being exported to the U.S.A. This means that green harvesting has a dual purpose here and usually takes place at "veraison" when the grapes are just starting to take on colour. A "lutte raisonnée" approach is adopted, overseen by the Chambre d'Agrlculture.

Vinification: White wines are cold settled, with temperature-controlled fermentation and membrane filtration for the moelleux. They are vinified in tank with no use of oak.

Visits: Open every day except Sundays and public holidays from 9 a.m. to 12 a.m. and 2 p.m. to 6 p.m. French and English spoken. Visits to the winery, walks round the vineyard and tasting with local specialities every Tuesday morning in July and August from 10.00 a.m. to 12.30 p.m.

History: The Domaine du Siorac has been in the Landat family since 1818. Jean-Paul is a fourth generation winemaker and prefers to make honest traditional Bergerac rather than expensive cuvées. 85% of the production is sold direct to customers.

The Wines: Bergerac Rouge Haute Cuvée
Bergerac Sec Tradition

Comments: The Bergerac Sec has been Hachette recommended for its fine Sauvignon qualities and stood out for us too. Brilliant pale lemon in colour with a grassy Sauvignon nose and a palate that was citrus fruits but with hints of tropical fruits also, this was a great example with fresh mouth-watering acidity, excellent balance and wonderful value.

In the U.K.: Not available.

Château Tertres du Plantou

Owner/Winemaker: Daniel & Josiane Bellugue
Address: Le Plantou, 24560 Boisse
Tel: (0)5 53 58 75 06
Fax: (0)5 53 58 75 06
Email: tertresduplantou@wanadoo.fr
How to get there: From Bergerac take the N21 Agen road as far as Colombier where you turn left on the D14 towards Issigeac. From Issigeac take the road towards Villeréal and after 5 km you come to Le Plantou which is just off the D14 to the right.
Appellations: Bergerac Rouge, Sec, Rosé, Côtes de Bergerac

Price: Band B
Vineyard: 16 hectares planted with Merlot, Cabernet Sauvignon and Cabernet Franc, and for the whites, Sauvignon and Sémillon. Vines are aged about 15 years for the whites and 25 for the reds.
Terroir: On hillside sites, the shallow soils are clay and limestone.
Viticulture: Daniel has been using organic methods since 1993 and is working towards Ecocert certification. Vines are planted at 5000 to the hectare and oats are grown between rows which, when cut down, form a mulch which is rich in potassium. Yields are low at 45 hl/ha for the Bergerac and 35 hl/ha for the Côtes de Bergerac Rouge.
Vinification: The reds are cold macerated for up to 7 days before fermentation, with maturation in tank or French oak barriques for up to 20 months in the case of the Côtes. The whites have a cold maceration for 24 hours before fermentation in stainless steel.
Visits: Every day from 10.00 a.m. to 7.00 p.m. French and English spoken. Josiane speaks good English and visits and tastings are particularly suitable for families as children are catered for.
History: From a farming background, Daniel Bellugue left his village of Boisse to work in a bank but eleven years later returned to his roots when he bought a property including just one hectare of vines. After a period of training and a programme of replanting, Daniel acquired a parcel of old vines at Le Plantou in 1996. Two years later he was joined by his wife Josiane who up till then had been a Deputy Head in a local school. As a result of a serious fall, she was unable to walk for six months and this gave her the time to involve herself in the business and she is now responsible for all the administration and marketing. All the production is sold directly to the consumer and there is no export.
The Wines: Bergerac Rouge
                Côtes de Bergerac
Comments: It would be a good idea to link this visit with a trip to the nearby bastides of Issigeac, Villeréal and Beaumont. The wines are worth a detour, especially the reds we tasted. The Bergerac Tradition was a good example of a straightforward Bergerac red, good deep colour with gutsy blackcurrant fruit, firm tannins and a chalky dry finish of decent length. The Cabernet-dominated Côtes de Bergerac was deep and dense in colour, with complex aromas of liquorice, tobacco and smoke, warm and spicy dark fruit flavours with excellent balance of tannins and acidity.
In the U.K.: Not available.

Château Tour de Grangemont

Owner/Winemaker: Christian Lavergne

Address: 24560 Saint Aubin de Lanquais

Tel: (0)5 53 24 32 89

How to get there: Leave Bergerac on the N21 towards Castillonnès and after 3 km. look out for a left-hand turn to Saint Nexans. Join the D19 as far as Saint Aubin. Turn left on the Mouleydier road and the property is 500m on the left.

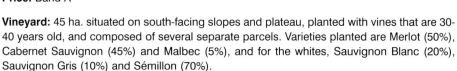

Appellations: Bergerac, Côtes de Bergerac

Price: Band A

Vineyard: 45 ha. situated on south-facing slopes and plateau, planted with vines that are 30-40 years old, and composed of several separate parcels. Varieties planted are Merlot (50%), Cabernet Sauvignon (45%) and Malbec (5%), and for the whites, Sauvignon Blanc (20%), Sauvignon Gris (10%) and Sémillon (70%).

Terroir: Clay-limestone with some gravel and siliceous soils.

Viticulture: In the vineyard, alternate rows are either grassed down or ploughed. The vines are planted 3300 to the hectare and are trained on the double Guyot system. Yields are 45 to 50 hl/ha for both reds and whites and harvesting is by machine.

Vinification: Maceration on the skins for 24 hours and cool fermentation are the norm for the whites with some use of micro-oxygenation for the reds and certain cuvées are aged in oak. The barrel cellar contains 230 barriques of which 20% are new. The moelleux is made from grapes which are "passerillés", i.e. allowed to dry on the vine, and which may be affected by noble rot.

Visits: By arrangement. French spoken and a little English and Spanish.

History: Christian Lavergne comes from a long line of winemakers and has been here for over 40 years. It was he who planted the noble grape varieties and created the winery. His son Fabien is an agronomist and oenologist.

The Wines: Côtes de Bergerac Rouge
                  Bergerac Blanc Sec
                  Bergerac Rosé

Comments: We tasted two reds from the 2005 vintage. The Bergerac was dense in colour with spice and liquorice on the nose and rich brambly fruit in the mouth with tannins still evident on the finish. The Côtes de Bergerac was in the same style with added oak sophistication and plenty of blackcurrant fruit with soft dry tannins.

In the U.K.: Not available

Vignoble des Verdots

Owner/Winemaker: David Fourtout
Address: 24560 Conne de Labarde
Tel: (0)5 53 58 34 31 **Fax:** (0)5 53 57 82 00
Email: verdots@wanadoo.fr
How to get there: Take the N21 from Bergerac towards Agen/Castillonnès. After 6 or 7 kilometres, take a left turn to Conne de Labarde.
Appellations: Bergerac Rouge, Sec, Rosé; Côtes de Bergerac; Monbazillac
Price: Band B/C
Vineyard: 96 hectares which border the eastern edge of the Monbazillac appellation. Merlot, Cabernet Sauvignon, Cabernet Franc and Malbec are planted for the reds, Sémillon, Sauvignon and Muscadelle for the whites.
Terroir: The vineyard is 3 kilometres in length and enjoys a variety of terroirs; stony limestone, clay and limestone, clay and silica, clay only.
Viticulture: Planting density is being increased to 6500 vines per hectare in order to produce lower yields per vine and more concentrated wines. Vines over 10 years old are grassed down, the rows between young vines are ploughed and those at the intermediate stage are grassed down every other row. Organic composts are used and David's approach is "sustainable viticulture" which comes somewhere between "lutte raisonnée" and organic. Yields are 35-40 hl/ha.
Vinification: David has built a new state-of-the-art winery with specially designed stainless steel conical fermentation tanks. Grapes are moved by conveyor belt to the tanks so there is no pumping and racking is done by gravity. Indigenous yeasts are used whenever possible. Along with Luc de Conti, David was the first to bring out a "Grande Cuvée" in 1995.
Visits: All year round. In July and August, 9.00 a.m. to 7.00 p.m. The rest of the year, 9.00 a.m. to 12.00 a.m. and 2.00 p.m. to 6.30 p.m., Monday to Saturday. Sundays by appointment. French, English, Spanish spoken.
History: The property was mentioned in the 1903 Féret guide under the name "Verdeau". David is a fourth generation winemaker, his family coming from Saint Emilion. He joined his parents in 1991 and along with his father Jean-Guy has realised the construction of a remarkable reception hall with cellars beneath and crossed by the Verdots river. Two chambres d'hôte have also been incorporated into one of the towers.
The Wines: Clos des Verdots
Château les Tours des Verdots
Grands Vins les Verdots
Le VIN selon David Fourtout
Comments: The Grand Vin Bergerac Sec had a hefty dollop of Sauvignon Gris as well as the 3 usual varieties and they married well to create an interesting wine with restrained nose of jasmine and orange blossom, followed by a complexity of tropical flavours, well-handled oak and a dry finish. The Bergerac was warm and spicy with a minty herbal nose and rich damson and blackberry palate balanced by pleasant acidity and tannins. However, it is worth letting David explain the play-on-words Verdots/verre d'eau (glass of water) which led to the naming of "Le Vin" and treating yourself to a bottle or two. This flagship wine is outstanding -rich and intense, mellow and creamy, robust black fruits with coffee and spice but well-balanced and not overblown.
In the U.K.: R.Bromley & Co., tel: 01494 776448 / Mr. Evans, tel: 01267 237348

Glossary

Anthocyans: Members of a group of natural chemical compounds which are responsible for the red colours of grapes and wines and are found in the grape skins.

Barrique: A type of barrel, most closely associated with the Bordeaux region, usually containing 225 litres.

Botrytis: A vine disease which is known as grey rot if it attacks unripe or damaged grapes or if it occurs in damp weather. However, the term is often used to indicate botrytis cinerea, or noble rot, which in the right conditions, is essential in the production of sweet white wines.

Boulbène: Not very fertile soil, sandy clay, red, yellow or grey, found in the Aquitaine basin.

Chai: A French word which, in general terms, means the building where the wine is made, the winery, and can include the "cuverie" where fermentation takes place and the barrel store.

Chaptalisation: The practice of adding sugar to the grape must before and/or during fermentation. It is quite common in more northerly parts of Europe in order to boost alcohol content in an unripe vintage.

Chef de culture: The person who is in charge in the vineyard.

Coulure: A form of poor fruit set in grapes when, soon after flowering, the small berries fall off. This is often caused by poor weather at flowering time and if excessive can drastically reduce yields.

Cretaceous: Term used in relation to limestone belonging to the uppermost system of the Secondary of Mesozoic rocks.

Cryoextraction: French term for freeze concentration. Freshly picked grapes are kept at about minus five degrees and then gently pressed. Only the very sweetest grapes will have remained unfrozen and will yield small amounts of very rich juice.

Cuvaison: French term generally used to describe the time a red wine spends fermenting in tank.

Cuvée: Literally a "tank-full" but often used to label a wine, usually of better quality, often matured in oak, from a particularly good vat of wine.

Débourbage: French term for the process of cold settling freshly drained and pressed white musts before fermentation.

Décavaillonnage: This is the process of ploughing beneath the rows of vines. It used to be an unpopular back-breaking job which nowadays is usually performed by an intercep machine.

Délestage: French term for the process of racking wine off its lees (soutirage) and returning it to the tank. As with racking in general, this is part of the clarification and aeration programme.

Demi-muid: Oak cask containing 600 litres.

E.A.R.L.: Abbreviation of Exploitation Agricole à Responsabilité limitée.

Féret: Originally published in 1903, the Féret guide to "Bergerac et ses Vins", updated in 1994, is the reference work par excellence for the region.

Fining: "Collage" in French, fining has the aim of clarifying and stabilizing a wine by removing particles with the help of a fining agent such as bentonite or egg-whites.

Foudre: Large oval barrel commonly used in Alsace.

G.A.E.C.: Abbreviation of Groupement Agricole d'Exploitation en Commun.

Grassing down: The process of planting grass or allowing grass to grow naturally between rows of vines. This has the effect of providing competition for the vines and thus reducing yields and also helps to counteract erosion.

Green harvesting: The removal of excess bunches of grapes during the summer months to prevent overcrowding, reduce yields and produce healthy, more concentrated fruit.

Guyot: Single or Double Guyot training in which canes are trained along horizontal wires with six to ten buds per cane.

Hectare: An area of 10,000 square metres which equates to about two and a half acres.

Hydromorphic: Water retaining.

Liquoreux: French term for very sweet dessert wines, often made from botrytised grapes.

Maître de chai: The person in charge of the winemaking, the cellarmaster.

Malolactic: Secondary fermentation in which more aggressive malic acid is converted into softer lactic acid. This will be encouraged in most red wines but in white wines in the Bergerac area, it does not normally take place so that the fresh acidity of the grape varieties can be retained.

Marc: French term for the grape pomace, the debris that is left, in the case of red wines, after fermentation. It is encountered in the phrase "sous marc" in connection with the micro-oxygenation process used with red wines, to indicate that the wine is still on its lees.

Marl: A sedimentary rock which is a combination of clay and limestone.

Micro-oxygenation: A process which introduces oxygen into a wine in a controlled manner. It can be used to avoid stuck fermentations and during the maturation process can soften tannins, avoid the formation of reductive flavours and too much pumping over. It may be that it reduces a wine's staying power and is often used in wines that are to be drunk young.

Mildew: Powdery mildew, also known as oidium, attacks all green parts of the vine and spreads in warm weather, being little affected by humidity. It has traditionally been treated by dusting with sulphur. Downy mildew is a fungal disease which spreads in warm and humid conditions. It is usually treated with copper-based fungicides such as Bordeaux mixture.

Millerandage: Abnormal fruit set with both large and small berries present in the same bunch.

Moelleux: French term describing wines which are generally medium-sweet.

Molasse: Thick sedimentary formation consisting of alternating sandy and silty beds.

Oenologist: Someone qualified in the science of winemaking though this may also extend to knowledge of viticulture. Often used as a consultant.

Oidium: See Mildew.

Périgord: Former French earldom which now corresponds more or less to the département of the Dordogne.

Phenolics: Also called polyphenols, a large group of chemical compounds which include colour pigments, natural tannins and many flavour compounds.

Photosynthesis: Biochemical reaction which combines water and atmospheric carbon dioxide, using the energy of the sun to form sugars in plants. Green chlorophyll pigments in vine leaves capture the sun's energy and the sugars formed are transported to the grapes. Photosynthesis is highest in warm sunny years.

Phylloxera: A root-feeding aphid which attacks only grapevines. At the end of the 19th century, it destroyed 6.2 million acres of vineyard in France.

Pigeage: French term for the action of punching down the cap of grape skins during fermentation to encourage extraction of colour and tannins and provide aeration. It can be done manually or mechanically.

Qualenvi: A qualification which encompasses service, quality and environmental reliability. Affiliation to Qualenvi would guarantee free guided tours, information and maps for the visitor, hygiene and quality controls, authenticity of the wines etc.

Remontage: French term for systems of pumping over, i.e. pumping fermenting juice over the cap in order to extract colour and tannins and to aerate the wine. See Pigeage.

Rognage: This is a trimming of the vines, usually by machine, which takes place perhaps four times a year. It's a bit like giving the vines a haircut and leaves the vineyard with that manicured look.

Saignée: Technique for making rosé wine by running off or "bleeding" free-run juice from red grapes after a short pre-fermentation maceration. This method also has the effect of concentrating the remaining red wine by increasing the ratio of skins to juice.

Siliceous: Sedimentary rocks rich in silica.

Tannins: Similar to anthocyans, tannins are present in grape skins, pips and stalks. Consequently they are encountered mainly in red wines and can be dry and astringent. Some grape varieties such as Cabernet Sauvignon are noticeably high in tannin. Tannins also come from maturation in oak and new oak in particular.

Tartrates: Harmless crystalline deposits which are mainly potassium acid tartrate which are sometimes seen in a bottle of wine. In white wines these tend to be settled out by cold stabilization and filtration.

Bibliography

French titles

Bergerac et ses vins, Marc-Henry Lemay, Editions Féret, 1994, Bordeaux.

Cartographie des sols viticoles du Bergeracois, ENITA de Bordeaux, Cartagère, Chambre d'Agriculture Dordogne, 2005.

Découvrir: Le Périgord, MSM 1993, Vic-en-Bigorre.

Les Vins de Bergerac: le Périgord pourpre, Michel Delpon, Dire éditions, 2001, Cahors.

Vin et Société à Bergerac, Jacques Beauroy, Anma Libri, 1976, Saratoga, California.

English titles

La Belle Saison, Patricia Atkinson, Arrow Books, 2006, London.

The Chronicles of Froissart, translated by John Bourchier, Macmillan, 1904, New York.

The Hundred Years War, Christopher Allmand, Cambridge University Press, 1988.

The Hundred Years War, Desmond Seward, Constable, 1978, London.

The Oxford Companion to Wine, ed. Jancis Robinson, Oxford University Press, 1994.

The Ripening Sun, Patricia Atkinson, Arrow Books, 2004, London.

Terroir, James E. Wilson, Mitchell Beazley, 1998, London.

Vines, Grapes and Wines, Jancis Robinson, Mitchell Beazley, 1986, London.

The Wines and Winelands of France; Geological journeys, Charles Pomerol, Robertson McCarta, 1989, London.

Wine from sky to earth, Nicolas Joly, translated by George C. Andrews, Acres U.S.A., 2005, Austin, Texas.

Wines of south-west France, Paul Strang, Kyle Cathie Ltd., 1996, London.

Index of Owners/Winemakers

A Page No.

Amécourt, Yves d' - 102
Atkinson, Patricia - 106

B

Barde family - 123
Baudry, Bertrand and Bernardette - 37
Bellugue, Daniel and Josiane - 133
Bernardinis, Thierry - 115
Biau, Philippe - 115
Borderie family - 60
Borgers, Christine - 55
Bosredon, Comte Laurent de - 65
Bouché, Françoise - 33
Bouché, Paul and Elise - 40

C

Carle, Pierre - 88
Carles, Isabelle - 112
Castaing, Fabien - 76
Castaing, Régis - 70
Chevallier, Sylvie - 71
Conti, Luc de - 62
Corbiac, Antoine Durand de - 35
Cuisset, Gérard - 98
Cuisset, Guy and Catherine - 93
Cuisset, Pascal - 91

D

Daulhiac, Thierry and Isabelle - 101
Deffarge, Jean-François and Sylvie - 119
Descoins, Franck - 110
Després, Thierry - 53
Dieuaidé, Sébastien - 54
Doughty, Richard - 103
Dubard family - 114
Dumonteil, Yannick - 67
Duperret, Daniel - 51
Durand brothers - 72

E

Page No.

Establet, Marcel and Marielle -   111
Evrard, Daniel -   100

F

Fauconnier, Bruno -   42
Feely, Sean and Caroline -   94
Feytout, Fabrice -   32
Fourtout, David -   135

G

Gaspard, Bernardette -   100
Geneste, Patrick and Bénédicte -   59
Gérardin, François, Benoît and Brigitte -   69
Gérardin, Patrick and Chantal -   96
Griaud, Kilian -   57
Guillermier, Thibaut -   117

H

Haseth-Möller, Philip de -   99
Hautefeuille, Catherine d' -   131
Hecquet, Daniel -   122

J

Jong, Helena de -   97

L

Lajonie, Joël and Alain -   39
Lambert, Olivier -   109
Landat, Jean-Paul -   132
Lansade, Régis -   34
Lavergne, Christian -   134
Lepoittevin-Dubost, Bertrand -   109
Lescure, Jean-Luc -   87

M	Page No.
Mähler-Besse, Christian -	118
Mallard, Philip and Marianne -	121
Martin, Charles -	89
Martrenchard family -	75
Maury, Nicole and Hervé -	39
Mayet, Alain and Marlène -	128
Monbouché, Michel -	74
Morand-Monteil, Gérôme -	41

O	
Ojeda, Jean-Luc and Emmanuelle -	66

P	
Pascal, Franck -	112
Passemar, Bertrand de -	79
Péronnet, Alain and Nathalie -	120
Piazzetta, Jean-Marc and Thierry -	85
Prouillac, Michel -	77
Prugne, Gilles -	92

R	
Rebeyrolle, Jean and Evelyne -	124
Rigal, Jean-Paul and Thierry -	86
Robbins, Julian -	116
Roche, Christian -	47
Roches, Didier -	38
Roches, Olivier -	104
Rondonnier, Gilbert -	49
Ryman, Hugh -	56

S	
Sadoux, Pierre-Jean -	90
Saint-Exupéry, François-Xavier de -	43
Saléon-Terras, Robert -	34
Saury family -	68
Savignac, Julien de -	52
Sergenton family -	73
Soulier, Brigitte and Jean-Philippe -	78
Sroka, Viviane -	113
Suyrot, Fabrice and Catherine -	81

T	Page No.
Thomassin, Pascal and Sylvie -	130

V	
Vergniaud, Jean -	129
Vesselle, Vincent -	61
Vidal family -	48
Villette, Guy -	54
Vurpillot, Emmanuel -	95

Index of Properties

A   Page No.

Ancienne Cure (Domaine de l') -   47

B

Beauportail (Château) -   32
Belingard (Château) -   65
Bloy (Château du) -   109
Bois de Pourquié (Domaine du) -   128
Borderie (Château) -   48
Borie Blanche (Domaine de la) -   66
Boyer (Domaine du) -   67
Brandeaux (Domaine les) -   85
Breil (Le Clos du) -   129
Briand (Château) -   49
Brie (Château La) -   50
Brunet Charpentière (Château) -   110

C

Cantonnet (Domaine du) -   86
Castellat (Domaine du) -   87
Chabrier (Château le) -   88
Champarel (Château) -   33
Chemins d'Orient (Les) -   34
Cluzeau (Château) -   68
Colline (Château de la) -   89
Combet (Domaine de) -   51
Corbiac (Château) -   35
Court-les-Müts (Château) -   90
Coutancie (Domaine de) -   36

E

Envège (Clos l') -   52
Eyssards (Château des) -   91

F

Fayolle (Château de) -   92
Fagé (Château le) -   69

G

	Page No.
Grand Jaure (Domaine du) -	37
Grande Maison -	53
Grange Neuve (Domaine de) -	70
Grimardy (Domaine de) -	111
Grinou (Château) -	93

H

Haut Bernasse (Château) -	54
Hauts de Caillevel (Château les) -	71
Haut Garrigue (Château) -	94
Haut-Lamouthe (Château) -	72
Haut Montlong (Domaine du) -	73
Haut Pécharmant (Domaine du) -	38
Haut Pezaud (Château du) -	55

J

Jaubertie (Château de la) -	56
Jonc Blanc -	112
Julien (Château) -	113

K

Kalian (Château) -	57

L

Ladesvignes (Château) -	74
Lardy (Château) -	95
Laulerie (Château) -	114

M

Mallevieille (Château de la) -	115
Masburel (Château) -	116
Masmontet (Château) -	117
Maurigne (Château la) -	96
Mayne (Château le) -	75

M	Page No.
Mège (Clos du) -	97
Merles (Château les) -	39
Miaudoux (Château) -	98
Michel de Montaigne (Château) -	118
Monbazillac (Château de) -	58
Monestier la Tour (Château) -	99
Moulin Caresse (Château) -	119
Moulin Garreau (Château) -	120
Moulin Pouzy (Domaine de) -	76

N	
Neyrac (Château) -	40

P	
Panisseau (Château de) -	100
Payral (Château le) -	101
Pech Bessou (Clos du) -	130
Perrou (Château) -	102
Petit Paris (Domaine du) -	59
Pique-Sègue (Château) -	121
Poulvère (Château) -	60
Prouillac (Domaine) -	77
Puy-Servain (Château) -	122

R	
Rayre (Château la) -	61
Raz (Château le) -	123
Ressaudie (Château la) -	124
Richard (Château) -	103
Robertie (Château la) -	78

S	
Saintongers d'Hautefeuille (Château les) -	131
Sanxet (Château de) -	79
Sigoulès (Cave de) -	80
Siorac (Domaine du) -	132

T	Page No.
Tap (Château le) -	104
Terrasses (Clos des) -	81
Terre Vieille (Château) -	41
Tertres du Plantou (Château) -	133
Tilleraie (Château) -	42
Tiregand (Château de) -	43
Tour de Grangemont (Château) -	134
Tour des Gendres (Château) -	62

U	
Union Vinicole Bergerac-Le Fleix -	125

V	
Verdots (Vignobles des) -	135
Vigiers (Château des) -	105

Y	
Yvigne (Clos d') -	106

About the Author

Phil Hargreaves has worked as a linguist for the past forty years and a wine merchant for the last twenty. He has been able to wear both his hats simultaneously in the realisation of this guide. He started in the wine trade importing wine from Alsace and was invited to become a member of the Confrérie St. Etienne d'Alsace for his work in promoting their wines. He currently runs the Premier Cru Wine Club and the Hengate Wine School in the East Riding of Yorkshire, having also taught languages in the county in both Beverley and Bridlington. This is his first book.

Notes

Notes

Notes

Notes

Notes

Notes

Notes